KEEPING UP WITH TIME

Dr Anisur Rahman

ISBN: 978-1-8384686-1-3

Published By: -

i2i Publishing. Manchester.
www.i2ipublishing.co.uk

Dedication

In memory of my loving sister who sadly passed away about five months ago (in April 2021) as the victim of Covid-19.

This book is also in remembrance of millions of Covid-19 victims around the world.

CONTENTS

On Religion

Preface

At the present time, we see that facts are quite often manipulated and even manufactured to suit the purposes of the presenter. The molestation of facts, which is generally called the 'alternative truths', alters the perception of events and makes readers deeply suspicious of the authenticity of events. So, there is a need to bring out unadulterated basic facts so that readers can whet their appetite with truth. This book, *Keeping up with Time*, is an attempt to keep the discerning readers abreast with modern day issues, bare facts, basic analyses and unbiased opinions.

A wide variety of topical issues, articles, essays and blogs were published by the author in various newspapers in the UK, USA, Canada, India and Bangladesh. Each one of these topics deals with issues where only factual and verified information was used and, as far as possible, complex issues have been dissected, simplified and explained in a clear and succinct way for the readers.

As the topics selected are articles and blogs, they are short, sharp and to the point and within the readers' attention span of 1200 to 1600 words. The wide range of topics has been divided into three sections entitled 'On Science and Technology', 'On Global Issues', and 'On Religion'. Each section has its own Glossary of Terms where difficult and unfamiliar terms and items have been explained, so that the topics in that section can be fully appreciated.

In the 'On Science and Technology' section, a wide range of technical issues of interest such as the black hole, gravitational waves, dark matter and dark energy, everything from nothing, entropy and the arrow of time etc. are presented. The most up to date information and research results have been incorporated and presented in a clear and succinct way.

In the 'On Global Issues' section, topics such as the inequality and inequity in capitalism, Solzhenitsyn's views on communism, Tagore's philosophical views, frailty in democracy, Orwellian dystopia, the illusion of reality, human population and many more are presented. As can be seen, some of the articles deal with historical events, while others look to the future.

In the 'On Religion' section, topics such as science and Islam, religion and morality, religious excesses in Islam, Einstein's views on religion, the brutality of religious fanatics etc., are covered. In this section, views and opinions have been expressed somewhat provocatively; some readers may find that somewhat abrasive. But that was the purpose – to shake out the age-old views to bring people out of their comfort zones. But scrupulous attempts have been made to use only verified information and views.

ON SCIENCE AND TECHNOLOGY

Classical physics to modern physics

Classical physics was the mainstream physical science until about 1900, when all day-to-day physical problems could be explained within this discipline. It was developed over the centuries by Chinese, Indian, Greek (Archimedes) and Arab (al-Biruni) scientists right up to the period of Copernicus, Newton and beyond. But gradually it ran into difficulties as new, technically challenging phenomena started to emerge due to the invention of new equipment and instruments and as more reliable and accurate measurements were made.

Classical physics was made up of a number of broad-brush disciplines such as: (i) Newtonian physics dealing with Newton's laws of motion, gravitational forces of nature attracting bodies, properties of matter etc.; (ii) Optics dealing with light travelling through space or through transparent media like waves and interacting with matter, producing a spectrum of light; (iii) Heat and Thermodynamics dealing with heat moving from hot to cold bodies like water flowing from higher to lower levels, steam engines, entropy etc and (iv) Atomic physics dealing with microscopic structures of matter called atoms and the interactions of atoms. All these subject matters were carefully researched, analysed, scrutinised and applied to real life and the results were firmly engraved in the minds of scientific people who believed they had achieved everything that could be achieved in physical science.

In 1874, a bright young boy by the name of Max Planck, aged sixteen, approached his physics teacher seeking his advice about the prospect of building a career in physics. He was told that it was hardly worth entering physics anymore as everything there was to discover in physics had already been discovered and that the only things remaining were to evaluate physical constants to higher levels of accuracy! However, the young Max Planck, undaunted, pursued his physics career and in just over 25 years' time, he produced (almost unknowingly) the revolutionary concept of the quantisation of light energy which explained *black body radiation* and that ushered in more advanced physics called modern physics.

Modern physics may be seen as comprising two parallel but distinctive branches of physics: (i) quantum mechanics which deals with extremely small entities such as atoms, electrons, photons and other sub-atomic particles, which are generically called quantum particles, and (ii) the theory of relativity which deals with space-time continuum. It may be noted at the outset that both of these branches of science were initiated and advanced by one of the greatest minds that physics had produced in the 20th century, Albert Einstein. We will discuss these two branches sequentially.

Although Max Planck was the first to venture outside the conventional concept of light being wave in nature to explain black body radiation in 1900, it was Albert Einstein who gave scientific explanation by proposing in 1905 the 'quantisation' of light – a phenomenon where light was assumed to consist of discrete packets of energy – which he called the quantum of light or the *photon*. This quantum of light was advanced in order to explain the hitherto inexplicable photoelectric process, where light was allowed to fall on the surface of a metal and electrons were emitted and then detected. No matter how long or how intense one type of light was, electrons would not be emitted. Only when light of higher frequencies was allowed, electrons were emitted. Einstein showed that photons (quantum of energy in a bundle) of higher frequencies have higher energies and those higher energy photons could dislodge and emit electrons bound to their shells with certain energies. For this quantisation theory, Einstein was awarded the Nobel prize in 1921.

Despite the fact that Einstein was the pioneer of the quantisation of light, he was not at ease with the way this new concept had been taken up by 'new lions' of quantum mechanics under the stewardship of physicists like Niels Bohr, Wolfgang

2

Pauli, Werner Heisenberg, Erwin Schrodinger, Max Born and many more in the early part of the last century. They collectively produced the full-blown quantum mechanics and produced what they called the 'Copenhagen Interpretation' of quantum mechanics, which Einstein had difficulty reconciling.

The other strand of classical physics was *Newton's law of gravity*. It tells us that two bodies attract each other by a force called gravitational force. This attractive force makes the smaller body move towards the larger body and hence an apple was pulled towards the earth, as Newton had observed. These are quite sensible and intuitive concepts in nature. But then nearly 250 years later, Einstein produced the theory of gravity (special and general) which swept away Newton's concept of gravitational force.

Newton visualised that gravitational force between bodies diffuses through space but did not produce any scientific explanation of how this force propagates. The electromagnetic force is technically real as electric and magnetic fields interact with each other and propagate through space, but the gravitational force had no scientific basis for its propagation.

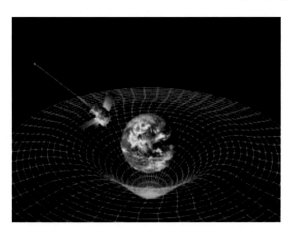

Figure 1.1.   The theory of relativity predicts that gravity curves space

Einstein proposed that the gravitational field bends and warps space - more like a heavy body on a trampoline – as shown in Figure 1.1 and other bodies follow the curvature. When there is a large number of bodies warping the space, the space becomes jagged and celestial bodies move around in tortuous paths. The gravitational field is the space itself. Space and time are intricately interlinked. Without gravity, there would be no space-time. Nearly one hundred years after Einstein's theory of relativity, experimental evidence of the gravitational field and the gravitational wave have been produced by the *LIGO* (Laser Interferometer Gravitational-wave Observatory) experiment, showing that space is modulated by the gravitational field.

Einstein's theory of relativity has many other profound implications. An important one is that the speed of light is inviolable, it is constant, and it is the ultimate limiting speed. No object, however energetic, can travel faster than light. For example, if we could travel faster than light, then we could go back in time (to the past), which is absolutely mind-boggling. (One conundrum is that if someone could travel back in time, say to the time when his father was a boy, and kill his father before he was even born, then this time-traveller would not exist and his father could not be killed and so this time traveller would come to exist! This circular conundrum could only be solved if nothing can travel faster than light or go back in time).

It is not only that one cannot travel faster than light; one's time span, or more precisely the passage of time, is dependent on one's position. For example, a man at the top of a mountain will find his watch moving faster than the person at sea level and so for the man on the mountain time moves faster (although the difference would be miniscule in small earthly mountains). Thus, a man living at sea level would find his twin sibling living high up in the mountain is slightly older than him!

An important outcome of the theory, for which Einstein is quoted regularly, is that mass and energy are equivalent ($E = mc^2$). The mass of a body can be converted to energy and vice versa. In the reactor of a nuclear power plant, the mass of fissile material (U-235 or Pu-239 or other fissile material) is converted to thermal energy which is then transformed into electrical energy. In a nuclear bomb, a small amount of nuclear material is converted to an enormous amount of energy. If the mass of ordinary material, say a human body, could be converted to energy, then even a rickety man could have enough energy in his body to supply the whole world with energy for the next few thousand years!

Newton's gravitational force in which all heavenly bodies attract each other is not an intrinsic property of material bodies, it is a quirk of nature in our observable universe. Two bodies with different physical properties could well repel each other. Indeed, there are prevailing ideas that the universe is replete with materials which repel each other and hence the universe is expanding.

Thus, space, as we understand, is the physical embodiment of the gravitational field. If there were no gravitational field, there would be no space. Space, like any other force field, like electromagnetic or nuclear, is discrete, quantised and granular. The quantum of space is so small that we cannot feel its discreteness, as we cannot feel the discreteness of atoms in a solid body.

The implication of Einstein's space is that, at the very beginning when even the *'Big Bang'* had not taken place, there was no space and no time. Space-time came into existence following that Big Bang, when gravity came into play, along with other forces such as electromagnetic force, strong nuclear force and weak nuclear force. If at the end, as physics predicts, the whole universe starts to collapse, there would be what is called the *'Big Crunch'.* The Big Crunch, being the reverse of the Big Bang, is when space-time would collapse and disappear completely. There will be nothing, no material, no space and no time. Then following that Big Crunch (when there would be no space and no time), there could be another Big Bang on 'quantum fluctuation'. But this is a pure speculation. Physics has not advanced far enough now to predict anything beyond the Big Crunch. What would be the nature and properties of sub-atomic and atomic particles, how they would interact and form material bodies etc., are all unknown at the moment.

From Newton's gravitational law to Einstein's gravitational waves

Figure 1.2   Cartoonist's depiction of Newton's gravitational force

In the summer of 1666, a young Cambridge University physics student by the name of Isaac Newton was sitting under an apple tree in his mother's garden at Woolsthorpe Manor in Lincolnshire, England. An apple fell from the tree onto the ground and that triggered him to question why the apple came down straight to earth and did not go sideways or upwards. That question led him to delve deeper into the mystery of attraction between two bodies and to come up with the law of gravity. He published his research work in *The Principia Mathematica* in 1687, where he described, among other things, this seminal work on the law of universal gravitation.

This law of gravitation tells us that two bodies attract each other with a force which is proportional to the product of the masses of the bodies and inversely proportional to the square of the distance between them. This simple empirical formula was astonishingly successful in calculating the force of attraction between two bodies on earth. This law was also applied to calculate the attractive force between the earth and the moon and to the orbital motion of the moon around the earth. The law was quite accurate in defining the orbits of many other celestial bodies, although in a few cases the law was somewhat inaccurate.

This law was and still is the centrepiece of what is now known as 'classical physics' or 'Newtonian physics'. We all studied this law, Newton's laws of motion, properties of matter, electricity and magnetism, heat and thermodynamics, optics etc. in our schools and they provided the grounding for advanced physics.

For over 300 years, this law was supreme and explained how the force of gravity controls the motions of all celestial bodies. However, the law did not say anything about the nature of this force or how the force is propagated through space; it just stated that the force diffuses through space without leaving any trace. As the predictions of the law were correct in most of the cases, physicists did not bother too much about these minor details and even ignored some minor discrepancies.

At the turn of the 20th century, a patent clerk by the name of Albert Einstein was working on patent submissions of electrical devices in Bern, Switzerland as a 'Technical Expert, Third Class' and in his spare time he was working on gravitational problems. The Patent Office work took up 48 hours of his time per week over six days. Einstein described his workload, stating that it left him with '*eight hours for fooling around each day and then there is also Sunday!*'

In 1905 he published a technical paper outlining the *Special Theory of Relativity,* supplying revolutionary scientific ideas and concepts. In this paper, he introduced two fundamental concepts: the principle of relativity and the constancy of the speed of light. The speed of light was stated to be independent of the speed of the observer. In other words, whether the observer moves in the direction of light or opposite to it, he would see the speed of light always remaining constant (c= 3x10^8 m/s). It may be mentioned that in 1905, Albert Einstein produced three more monumental papers of enormous significance: (i) the mass-energy equivalence (E=mc^2), (ii) the Brownian motion of small particles, and (iii) photoelectric effects. His work on photoelectric effects, for which he was awarded a Nobel prize in 1921, showed the particulate nature of light, which laid the foundation for quantum mechanics. As mentioned above, the year 1905 was extremely productive for Albert Einstein.

Einstein developed his relativity concept even further and produced the *General Theory of Relativity* in 1916. In this General Theory of Relativity, he advanced the principle of space-time, not space and time. He stipulated that the three dimensions of space (such as X, Y and Z dimensions in cartesian coordinates) and one dimension of time are not independent of each other, but intricately linked to form a single, four-dimensional space-time continuum.

This concept of space-time continuum was revolutionary at that time and even now it baffles human beings. The relativistic consideration has produced what is now called time dilation. The passage of time is relative and so it depends on the motion of an observer relative to a stationary observer. Also, the passage of time depends on the location in a gravitational field. For example, a clock attached to an observer in a travelling spaceship will tick slower than a clock attached to an observer in a stationary position. Also, a clock in a higher gravitational field, such as at the surface of Earth, will tick slower than that of a clock in a lower gravitational field such as the top of a mountain.

Let's take an example. There were three men in the UK, all of them exactly the same age, say, 25 years. They decided to offer themselves as guinea pigs for a research on gravity. One was asked to stay in Lincolnshire, England (not too far from Newton's famous apple tree), the other was told to go and live high up in the Himalayan mountains and the third, the most

9

adventurous of the lot, got the opportunity to travel through space in a superfast spaceship. The spaceship travelled fast and so his clock was ticking slowly. Let's say his spaceship was so fast that one year in the spaceship clock was equal to five Earth years and the mountain man clocked 10 minutes more in the five years than the Lincolnshire man. When after five Earth years they met on Earth, they found that the mountain man was 10 minutes older than 30, Lincolnshire man was exactly 30 Earth years of age, and the spaceship man was a whopping four years younger than 30! To the spaceship man, it would seem that he had gone forward four years in the future when he came back to Earth!

Figure 1.3   Warping of space by celestial bodies

Einstein stipulated that the gravitational field creates space and bodies with masses bend and warp space; more like massive bodies create curvature in a trampoline, see Figure 1.3. All smaller bodies fall into the curvature in the trampoline created by the massive bodies. When there is a large number of bodies warping the space, the space becomes jagged and celestial bodies move around in tortuous paths. There is no force of gravity pulling objects towards each other; just the bodies moving around the jagged curved space along the path of least resistance.

Space, like any other force field, is discrete, quantised and granular. The quantum of space is dubbed a *graviton,* similar to the term *photon* in the electromagnetic field, and it is so small that we cannot feel its discreteness, as we cannot feel the discreteness of photons of light or the discreteness of atoms in a solid body.

Exactly one hundred years after Einstein's General Theory of Relativity, experimental evidence of the gravitational field and the gravitational wave have been produced by the *LIGO (Laser Interferometer Gravitational-wave Observatory)* experiment and have shown that space is modulated by the gravitational field. A monochromatic laser beam of light was split and sent at right angles to each other along two arms, each 4 km long. These beams were reflected back along the same path and allowed to interfere back at source. If there is no distortion or modulation of the path lengths, the two beams would interfere in anti-phases and there would be no interference patterns. On the other hand, if path lengths are distorted, there would be interference patterns.

When two super massive black holes some 1.3 billion *light years* away merged and produced a gigantic, massive black hole, an enormous amount of energy, equal to three solar masses, was produced and sent out as gravitational energy. It rippled through the whole universe in the form of the gravitational wave at the speed of light and deformed the space-time fabric. That deformation in space-time was detected by the LIGO experiment in the form of an interference pattern and that proves that gravitational waves modulate space.

At the very beginning, before even the *'Big Bang',* there was no space-time. Space-time came into existence following the 'Big Bang', when gravity came into play, along with the other three forces of nature - electromagnetic force, strong nuclear force and weak nuclear force. When at the end, the whole universe starts to collapse, there would be what is called the *'Big Crunch'* and space-time would collapse too and disappear. There will be nothing, no material, no space and no time. These are the predictions of scientific theories that exist today.

In 1930, when Einstein came to London as a guest of honour at a fundraising dinner to help the East European Jews, George Bernard Shaw, the chief guest, said humorously, "*Ptolemy made a universe which lasted for 1400 years. Newton made a universe which lasted for 300 years. Einstein has made a universe, and I can't tell you how long that will last.*" The audience laughed loudly, but none louder than Einstein!

Einstein's incredible burst of creativity in 1905

Figure 1.4   Three ages of Einstein

Albert Einstein, the iconic physicist of the twentieth century, was born at a time when prevailing physical science was deemed inadequate and incapable of explaining many emerging scientific facts and, worst of all, there was nothing on the horizon to replace it or improve on it. The scientific establishment of the day was nonetheless complacent with or resigned to this impasse. When Max Planck, the future pioneer of the quantum concept, approached his professor in Munich in 1879 at the age of 21 and expressed his desire to pursue a research career in physics, he was told by a patronising professor that there was hardly anything left in physics to be discovered!

Albert Einstein, an Ashkenazi Jew (secular in religious outlook), was born on Friday 14 March 1879 in the historic city of Ulm, Kingdom of Wurttemberg, in the then German Empire. His father, being an engineer and a salesman, gave little Einstein every encouragement and adequate backing to pursue a technical career. He was very inquisitive and tenacious. There was nothing he would consider as unattainable. As a child he wondered if he could ride on a beam of light! He said about himself years later, *"God gave me the stubbornness of a mule."*

As a child he was not a prodigy by any standard. But as a headstrong boy, he intensely disliked strict disciplinarian life, either at school or at home. He would like to pursue his curiosity and his objectives with passion and energy. Years later, he said, *"Learn from yesterday, live for today, hope for tomorrow. The important thing is not to stop questioning".*

At the age of nine, when he was sent by his parents to Luitpold Gymnasium (a strict discipline-focussed school) in Munich, he was not happy at all. He intensely disliked the 'rote learning' method at the school with no opportunity for creative thinking. However, he pursued his studies there until the age of sixteen (in 1895) to keep his parents happy. But then to avoid compulsory military service in Germany, he left school and went to his parents in Italy at the end of 1895. After spending a few months with his parents in Italy, he was persuaded by them to continue with his secondary education in science at a Cantonal school in Zurich, Switzerland. He renounced his German citizenship in 1896, so that he would never be called for military service in Germany. He completed his studies and then graduated with a teaching diploma in physics and mathematics in 1900. During all these years, from 1895 to 1900, he was stateless. He acquired Swiss citizenship in 1901 after completing five years of residence there.

Aspiring to take up a career in physics, particularly at a university, was not easy at that time. He scaled down his ambition and for nearly two years he even tried to get a school teaching post, but without success. Eventually, on the recommendation of the father of his close friend, he managed to get a humble position at the Swiss Patent Office in Bern, capital of Switzerland, in 1902 as a 'Technical Expert – Third Class'. Although the position was lowly, the salary was quite handsome. This job, according to him, brought an end to "*the annoying business of starving*".

He moved to Bern in 1902 and lived there until 1907. Initially, as a bachelor, he rented a room beyond the river Aare, which meanders across the capital city of Bern. After he got married in 1903, he rented a two-bedroom apartment on the second floor of 49 Kramgasse in the picturesque Old Town part of Bern. The cobbled street of Kramgasse, with the famous clock tower on one side and the river Aare, some three hundred metres away (about two hundred metres from 49 Kramgasse) on the other, was one of the most beautiful streets in Bern. At the end of Kramgasse, a historic bridge led to the other side of the river. From the street level, a series of steps, some 200 of them, led to the riverbanks. Einstein used to sit and contemplate by the river in summer evenings as the rippling sound of crystal-clear water cascaded down the shallow river.

Einstein used to leave his apartment just before eight o'clock in the morning for a ten-minute walk to thé imposing Patent Office building. He said later in his life that his work as a Patent Clerk was only for 48 hours a week, and he had one additional day to spare! At work he had to look at the design details of electrical devices submitted by budding inventors. This required him to scrutinise details and identify any possible flaws. These traits and critical thinking honed his talent for future research in physics.

What inspired Einstein to write his first ground-breaking paper in 1905 advancing the proposal on the quantum theory of light was Max Planck's paper, detailing the solution of the black body problem with an outline of the hitherto unheard-of quantum concept of emission and absorption of light, a few years back. Einstein read the paper and was completely overwhelmed by this radical concept. Einstein carried forward that quantum idea and produced a paper on the photoelectric effects of light with the title 'On a Heuristic Point of View Concerning the Production and Transformation of Light' for the journal *Annalen der Physik*, the world's leading physics journal in Germany, and posted it on 17 March 1905. Max Planck happened to be the adviser on theoretical physics to the journal at that time. Despite Planck's reservation with Einstein's mind-boggling concept of the particulate nature of light, sweeping away the age-old concept of the wave nature of light, he allowed the paper to be published simply because of its radical nature.

Figure 1.5   Einstein with his mass-energy equivalence equation.

Einstein produced four papers between the dates of 17th March and 30th July 1905. The second one was from his PhD dissertation where he set out a way of determining the sizes of atoms. The third one was the explanation of the Brownian motion of atoms and molecules. The fourth one was, as Einstein himself admitted, a rough draft, 'On the Electrodynamics of Moving Bodies', giving details of the concepts of space and time. Max Planck read all of these papers, but when he read the last paper, he was simply blown away. Although Einstein did not call it 'the theory of relativity', Max Planck called it so and the title has stuck with it ever since.

Before the year was over, Einstein produced another paper, which contained a small equation, $E = mc^2$ (actually the equation was $E = mc^2/(\sqrt{(1-q^2/c^2)})$ where q was the speed of a body and c was the speed of light. If q was much smaller than c, then the term inside the square root became very close to 1 and hence $E = mc^2$). This equation came to be known as the mass-energy equivalence with which Einstein became synonymous. Also, during the same year, he reviewed as many as 21 technical books for the *Annalen der Physik* journal!

No other scientist, except perhaps Isaac Newton, had ever produced as many ground-breaking seminal pieces of work in such quick succession as Einstein did in 1905. He was only 26 at that time. Isaac Newton, an Englishman, at the age of 23 produced the gravitational law and advanced the theory of light, all in 1666! Oh yes, he also laid the foundation for calculus in the same year! It is amazing to note that these two prodigious physicists dealt with the same physical problems – the theory of gravity and the theory of light – with incredible ingenuity.

Einstein received the Nobel Prize in Physics in 1921 for his work on photoelectric effects of light. His work on the special theory of relativity (followed by the *general theory of relativity* in 1916) could also have warranted another Nobel Prize, but the concept was so profoundly mind-boggling and radical that even the Nobel Committee found it challenging without any supporting evidence! His mass-energy equivalence could have been another candidate for a Nobel Prize. He laid the foundations for two major planks of modern physics - quantum mechanics and the theory of relativity, all in the single year of 1905.

Quantum mechanics and the nature of reality

Quantum mechanics came into existence at the turn of the nineteenth century to the twentieth century, when many of the newly discovered experimental evidences could not be explained with the principles of classical physics. In 1900, Max Planck, in an attempt to explain *black body radiation,* advanced the concept that electromagnetic energy was absorbed and emitted in discrete lumps, which he called quanta (singular: quantum); that was the beginning of the quantisation of light. Albert Einstein laid the concept of quantisation on a firm footing in 1905 when he produced the theory of photoelectric effects and established *photons* as discrete particles - the smallest entity of radiation.

Light came to be viewed as both waves and particles, depending on experimental conditions, and hence the nomenclature 'wave-particle duality' came into the common vocabulary. If hitherto electromagnetic light can be viewed both as waves and particles, can particles (like electrons) behave like waves? This was the issue which de Broglie addressed in his PhD work and obtained the Nobel Prize for showing that it was indeed so. Wave-particle duality is a reality. If electrons are allowed to go through two slits, they interfere and produce alternate bright and dark spectral lines on a screen, exactly like light waves do. The microscopic world does not distinguish between waves and particles, they are blurred into indistinguishable entities. That is the nature that quantum mechanics has produced.

Heisenberg produced what came to be known as the *'Heisenberg uncertainty principle'.* The elementary particle like an electron cannot be measured with absolute precision in both its position and *momentum* at the same time. The act of measuring the position of an electron disturbs the complementary parameter such as velocity and so a certain amount of uncertainty in momentum creeps in - that is the uncertainty principle. Similar uncertainty exists when measuring the time and energy of the particle at the same time.

Electromagnetic waves propagate through space like waves, as water waves do on the surface of water, having crests and troughs. When two waves merge together in harmony, the crests and troughs join together and become larger (the amplitudes of two crests or two troughs add together); this is called constructive interference. On the other hand, if two waves merge in opposition, i.e. in anti-phase, the crests and troughs cancel each other and there will be no ripple, this is called destructive interference.

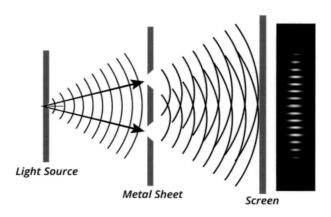

Figure 1.6   Double slit experiment with a light source

If a light source is placed in front of a double-slit barrier and the light is allowed to fall on a screen behind the barrier, the constructive and destructive interferences would show as interference fringes of bright and dark bands, as shown above in Figure 1.6. So, an interference fringe is a definitive proof of the wave nature of light - light diffracting through the double-slits. (Of course, light can also have a particulate nature, as shown in Einstein's photoelectric effects.)

20

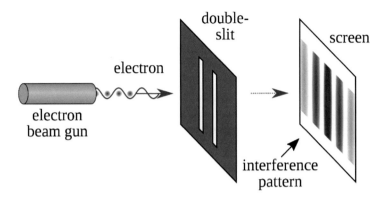

Figure 1.7   Interference pattern with very narrow slits

Now let us get back to the question of electrons. If electrons are fired from a source towards a screen and there is a double-slit barrier between the source and the screen, the screen should show the images of two slits on the screen. That is expected and perfectly normal, as the electrons are behaving like particles going through the slits and then striking the screen. Now if the slits are sufficiently narrowed down and the rest of the arrangement remains the same, what is then seen on the screen is a band of bright and dark bands, as if the electrons are behaving like waves producing interference patterns, see Figure 1.7. Now remembering de Broglie's wave-particle duality, this outcome would not be too surprising or outrageous!

Now let us make an arrangement where just one electron is fired at a time and let that electron have sufficient transit time to go through the slit and reach the screen. The electron can go through either of the two slits and one would expect that images of the slits would be produced on the screen if sufficiently large numbers of electrons are fired. But amazingly, an interference pattern appears on the screen!

This is bizarre. Remember that just one electron was fired at a time. Even if the electron behaved like a wave, then that electron-wave would just dissipate away as it reached the screen. It surely could not wait on the screen for the next electron-wave to come through and interfere with it!

Now, could that be that an electron somehow goes through both the slits simultaneously to produce an interference pattern on the screen? How could that happen and what is the physical mechanism to have one electron going through two slits at the same time? The other possible picture could be that half of an electron goes through one slit and the other half through the other slit and then they produce the interference pattern. But then what is the mechanism of splitting an electron into two halves to make an interference pattern? The whole thing becomes surreal, but the interference pattern is real.

Then the experimenter became more adventurous and thought that it would be worthwhile to find out exactly which way the electrons are going? Is an electron dividing itself to go through both the slits simultaneously? A detector was placed very discretely away from the path of the electron behind one of the slits. As an electron is negatively charged, the flow of the electron would produce a current and that current would produce a magnetic field. A detector had been designed to detect the magnetic field. The detector placed behind one of the slits would not affect the electron path or its flow in any way.

The same experiment was then conducted, but with a detector placed discretely behind one of the slits. What had been found on the screen? The interference pattern just disappeared completely! Yes, no bright and dark bands; only images of the slits on the screen! It was as if the electrons found out that they had been spied on and they decided not to behave like waves any more or go through both the slits simultaneously. If, on the other hand, the detector was taken away or turned off, the interference pattern returned! Science became supernatural!

These strange behaviours of electrons were so puzzling that even more than hundred years later (since this experimental evidence) nobody could give a complete and rational explanation. Quantum mechanics came into existence and has flourished since then, but no rational explanation of this bizarre electron behaviour had been produced. Nonetheless, quantum mechanics had produced an abstract mathematical formalism to explain this evidence.

In quantum mechanics, particles or waves are treated as wave functions (Schrodinger's wave equation). When there are two slits, two wave functions go through and interfere and that process is called quantum superposition. That superposition of waves produces interference patterns. Even one wave function – a mathematical formalism - can go through two slits and have superposition and produce an interference pattern.

In the quantum theory, particles like electrons revolving round the nucleus of an atom do not exist as particles. They are like strata of waves smeared round the nucleus. However, they exist, behaving like particles, when some energy is imparted to the atom or some energy is taken away from the atom resulting in those electrons moving up or down in energy levels. In other words, electrons exist only when there is an interaction or transition. Without such transitions, electrons just do not show up. However, electrons (with negative charge) are there around the nucleus, but there is no way of telling where the electrons are – only the probability of their presence (wave function) can be described! No wonder Einstein was not happy with such a description, which he called incomplete.

Niels Bohr, the high priest of quantum mechanics, and his group of fellow quantum physicists produced what is known as the 'Copenhagen Interpretation' of quantum mechanics. This interpretation advanced the idea that the sheer act of observation of quantum particles disturbed the character of electron-wave flow and that caused the waves to collapse into particles.

The Copenhagen Interpretation further emphasised that a quantum particle can only be said to exist when it is observed, if it is not observed it does not exist. This was a revolutionary concept, a provocative idea. Einstein could not reconcile with that idea. He retorted, "*When the Moon is there in the sky, it is real; whether one observes it or not.*" Thus, the great intellectual battle on the nature of reality ensued between Einstein and Bohr. Einstein firmly believed that quantum mechanics as it existed in his lifetime was inconsistent and incomplete (although he withdrew the 'inconsistent' branding, as quantum mechanics kept explaining modern technical processes with consistency). To prove the 'incompleteness' of quantum mechanics, he threw various 'thought experiments' at various times to challenge Bohr's Copenhagen Interpretation. Bohr countered those challenges with technical explanations, but Einstein was not fully convinced.

Quantum mechanics gives an abstract mathematical formalism of a system. It can predict quite accurately the correct outcome (such as electron fringes), but it does not or cannot give the physical picture of the path of the electron. In fact, the Copenhagen Interpretation insists that asking to know the path of the electron is superfluous and irrelevant. What is relevant is what happens when electrons reach the destination and quantum mechanics has the answer for that. That is the strength of quantum mechanics.

Einstein did not like the abstract nature of quantum mechanics. He always demanded that theory must mirror the reality; if not, it becomes a 'voodoo' science. For his persistent criticism, he was not very popular with the advocates of the Copenhagen Interpretation. They even asked, 'how is it possible that Einstein, who revolutionised the gravitational concept by saying that space is warped by gravity and the gravitational field is indeed the space, is now reluctant to accept ideas about quantum theory'?

Quantum mechanics had solved many intractable problems and predicted many physical aspects which subsequently came to be true. But, at the same time, it is incomprehensible, extremely abstract and devoid of 'elements of reality'. Anybody hoping to trace the theory mirroring reality would be totally disappointed. Even Richard Feynman, American Nobel laureate in Physics in 1965, who contributed significantly to the development of quantum physics (quantum electrodynamics) once retorted, "*I think I can safely say that nobody understands quantum mechanics.*" Nonetheless, quantum mechanics is the most advanced scientific discipline of today.

Entropy and the arrow of time

Heat, temperature, enthalpy, entropy, energy and so forth are quantities within the subject matter of thermodynamics and statistical mechanics in physics. These subject matters, along with general properties of matter, electricity and magnetism, optics, acoustics etc., were all bundled together as Newtonian physics or classical physics. This naming of classical physics does not imply that these subjects are 'classical', meaning they are old, outdated, antiquated subjects and hence there is nothing more to learn from them; far from it. It only means that these traditional subjects have been put together as a comprehensive whole in order to embrace the forthcoming newer disciplines, roughly from the beginning of the 20th century, such as the general theory of relativity, quantum mechanics, particle physics, cosmology etc., which are called the modern physics.

This traditional segregation of branches of physics into classical physics and modern physics is purely arbitrary. There is no strict boundary, no demarcation line, either in terms of time or disciplines between classical and modern physics. Entropy, the parameter which was invented in the 19th century as a thermodynamic quantity, has profound implications for the concept of the space-time continuum and the Big Bang theory of the modern physics.

First of all, we need to understand what heat is before we can go to understanding entropy. In the olden days - 17th century or earlier - people used to visualise heat as some sort of fluid called 'caloric'. This caloric was assumed to be composed of two parts – hot and cold. A body was hot because it had more hot caloric and less cold caloric. On balancing out the hot and cold caloric, there was a net hot caloric in the body. On the other hand, a body was cold because it had more cold caloric than hot caloric. These hot and cold calorics were perceived not as fluids, like water, but as some intrinsic properties of the bodies. But the flow of hot caloric to cold caloric was like water flowing from a higher level to a lower level. When hot and cold bodies came in contact with each other, hot caloric moved from the hot to the cold body, thereby rendering the cold body somewhat hotter.

During the industrial revolution, sparked by the advent of steam engines, scientists started to look at the roots of thermodynamics. The French engineer, Sadi Carnot, produced the Carnot cycle where heat always dissipated from hotter to cooler regions and anything against this trend required additional energy to power it. These scientists/engineers managed to identify a very important thermodynamic parameter called the 'temperature' that measures the body's 'hotness' or 'coldness'.

In reality, heat is the thermal energy which arises due to vibration, oscillation or physical motion of atoms and molecules that make up the body. When a body at a higher temperature comes in contact with another body at lower temperature, the excess vibrational energy of the atoms and molecules are transferred to the body at lower energy. It is the temperature that determines the direction of the flow of heat.

Let us now consider what entropy is. Entropy is a thermodynamic quantity that is defined as the ratio of the amount of heat energy that flows from one body (somewhat hotter) to another body (somewhat cooler) to the absolute temperature of the hotter body. As the probability of energy flowing from higher energy to the lower energy is much higher than the other way round, it has always been found that heat flows from a hotter body to a cooler body and entropy is assigned to be positive in that situation. Should heat flow from a cooler body to a hotter body – its probability being very low indeed - the entropy could theoretically be negative. But in nature, heat never flows from a cooler body to a hotter body and entropy is never negative. The very nature of heat is that it arises from motions of atoms and molecules and the extra energy is transferred from hotter to cooler bodies, thereby making cooler bodies' atoms and molecules a bit more excited and energetic. That extra energy in relation to absolute temperature is a measure of entropy; thus, entropy is a measure of disorder in the composite system. As disorder increases, so does entropy. It is shown in Figure 1.8.

It may be pointed out that when heat is shared between the bodies, it does not matter what the relative sizes of these bodies are. For example, a hot teaspoon dipped in a large bucket of water would have some amount of heat transferred from the spoon to the water, although the total amount of energy of the bucket of water may be much higher than that of the spoon. As stated above, it is the temperature that determines the flow of heat and thereby the increase in entropy.

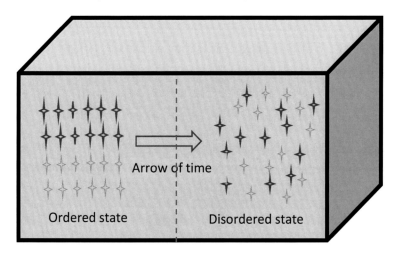

Figure 1.8   The degree of disorder and the arrow of time

This increase in entropy or the degree of disorder is asymmetrical i.e. it only moves in one direction. In that sense, entropy is like the arrow of time which only moves forward - from present to future. This concept of the arrow of time was developed by the British astrophysicist Arthur Eddington in

1927 when he was considering the dissipation of energy by microscopic bodies. From the previous example, the heat from the spoon is transferred to the bucket of water as time passes – entropy always increases with the arrow of time. A situation can hardly be visualised when heat flows in reverse, although theoretically it is possible with infinitesimally low probability. In the reverse heat flow, the dipped spoon would recover heat from the bucket and become hot again!

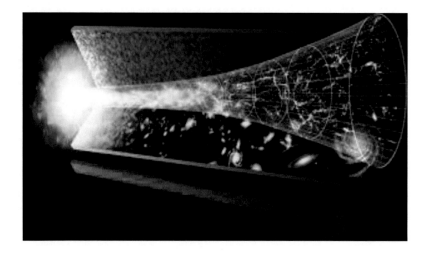

Figure 1.9   Unidirectionality of entropy and the arrow of time

From the time of the *Big Bang* (around 13.8 billion years ago), entropy has been going up, i.e. the degree of disorder has been spreading. That is quite natural as heat flows from the hotter part of the universe to another cooler part of the universe and this unidirectional increase in entropy is also the arrow of time.

This unidirectionality of entropy and the arrow of time also has profound implications on other branches of science. Let us take human aging and mortality, for example. With the advancement of medical/biological sciences, it has been anticipated that a time will come when human beings will live for a very long time and may even become immortal. Living longer with better medical care is feasible; in fact, it is already happening. People, on average, now live to almost double the age they used to a couple of centuries ago.

But being immortal means the human body will not age or decay in time and that means its past, present and future body structures and body functions would remain the same or very nearly the same! There would be no change in body conditions – no body growth, no body decay or flow of nutrients from one part of the body to another! It is a continuation of the same thing ad infinitum. In other words, human beings will live in suspended animation - neither alive nor dead – as their energy flow will stagnate to zero, meaning there is no change in entropy and no arrow of time. If that is what is meant by immortality, then that may, theoretically, be achievable. But, in reality, human beings, or for that matter any form of life, can never be immortal in the true sense of the term. A life can live for a long period of time and gradually decay, but it can never last forever.

The other scenario of immortality within the framework of entropy and the arrow of time is to recreate human beings at the end of normal human lives. If an old man is cloned, using his *stem cells*, then a new child can be born replicating the old man and thereby making him come alive again as a child – although he will not have the memory of the old man. Whether that process of replicating the old man physically can be considered immortality or not is subject to debate.

31

Everything from nothing!

Can everything that we see here on Earth and in the sky like comets, planets, stars, pulsars, galaxies, supernovae and so forth and the celestial bodies that we cannot see, such as black holes, dark matters etc., come from nothing? Can these bodies arise from an absolute vacuum, from empty space and can empty space pop up from nowhere? This sort of query, some might say, is an absurd, baseless, blasphemous endeavour; while others might say it is a profound scientific inquiry, outside the pigeon-holed mode of thinking.

Philosophers and theologians of all persuasions have tried to convince us that everything we see in the universe is from divine creation. But we must start off with certain fundamental assumptions – we have to first accept the existence of an all-powerful, omnipresent, omniscient entity called God or Yahweh or Allah and we cannot question his origin, his present whereabouts or his mode of creation etc. Based on these premises, the revelations, commandments etc. as stated in the 'Books', must be followed as ordered by the creator!

But science is unwilling to accept this precondition without any concrete evidence or verification. That is why there is a conflict between science and religion. As Richard Dawkins, Emeritus Fellow of New College, Oxford and Evolutionary Biologist said, "*I am against religion because it teaches us to be satisfied with but not understand the world.*"

Science has moved away from accepting the divine proclamation that human beings are at the centre of creation, Earth is at the centre of the universe and the Sun goes around the Earth. Scientific discoveries have proved many of these proclamations, if not all, are blatantly wrong.

Science explored material objects on Earth – from day-to-day objects to their physical and chemical composition, from physical objects to molecules to atoms to sub-atomic particles. On the smallest scale, quantum mechanics explored the origin of matter and anti-matter and on the mind-boggling expansive scale of the universe, and the general theory of relativity explored the stars, galaxies, black holes, wormholes, the universe and even the multiverse.

The theologians would protest vigorously if someone, be it a scientist or a science writer, tried to give the scientific explanation of something or everything coming from nothing. They would express their dissent by asking sternly, what is then the omnipresent, omniscient, divine power called God or Yahweh or Allah doing? Is He not the undisputed Creator of everything in this universe? For centuries, religions have been proclaiming and propagating this message relentlessly. Now any attempt to explain it otherwise, on the basis of scientific ideas and narratives, would be branded as atheism.

Nonetheless, science has progressed enough to give a rational explanation to the creation of everything from nothing. But, first, we must understand the scientific meaning of the term 'nothing'. In everyday language, nothing means the absence of anything. If we consider a volume of space having length, breadth and height, say, of 20cm each, in front of our eyes, we may say there is nothing - as there is no book, no pencil, no string, no fruit or anything else in that small volume and so, we may conclude, there is nothing. But then, we must recognise that there are millions and millions of air particles of various types in that volume that we cannot see, but we breathe all the time. So, there are things where we perceive to have nothing.

Let us take that air-tight glass case where obviously there are air particles along with air pollutants, allergens etc. Now if we pump out these particles very carefully using high quality pumps and make it an ultra-high vacuum, can we say that there is nothing in the glass case? No, we cannot say that there is nothing in the glass case and that is because modern physics shows us otherwise. Figure 1.10 depicts a situation where in the above-mentioned box, there is an absolute vacuum or ultra-high vacuum, but still there is evidence of weird particles and anti-particles and energies which are bubbling up all the time!

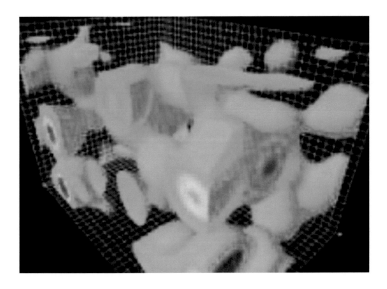

Figure 1.10   Quantum fluctuations in an absolute vacuum

The two branches of modern physics – the general theory of relativity and quantum mechanics – give us a description of physical processes which are mind-boggling, counter-intuitive and occasionally weird. Even Einstein, who single-handedly produced the general theory of relativity and pioneered quantum mechanics, had extreme difficulty in absorbing the full implications and interplay of these two theories.

Einstein produced the mass-energy equivalence ($E=mc^2$), a very elegant and at the same time extremely important equation. What it means is that the mass of an object such as an atom or a molecule or a large number of molecules in a ball or an apple or a pencil and so forth has an equivalent energy and conversely an amount of energy has an equivalent mass. It is not theoretical physicists' crazy idea, it has been found, in practice, in particle physics experiments, in radioactive decay and in nuclear reactors that mass and energy are interchangeable.

A certain amount of energy suddenly disappears, and a very small particle called an electron and its anti-particle, which is called a positron, appear. The electron is what we use to generate electricity and is used to run a television, radio, mobile phone etc., and in our everyday parlance, it is matter. On the other hand, a positron is anti-matter. When this matter (electron) and anti-matter (positron) come in contact, they annihilate each other in a flash and an amount of energy is produced instantly, which is exactly equal to what disappeared in the first place to produce this electron and positron pair.

Alongside this mass-energy equivalence, one may consider quantum physics' *Uncertainty Principle,* produced by Werner Heisenberg. We must remember that quantum mechanics deals with very small particles such as electrons, positrons, atomic and sub-atomic particles. The basic tenet of this principle is that we cannot simultaneously measure certain pairs of conjugate variables such as *energy and time* or *position and momentum* of a particle with absolute precision. The degree of inaccuracy or uncertainty of the pair of observables ($\Delta E.\Delta t$ or $\Delta p.\Delta x$) is always higher than a quantity called the Planck constant ($h/2\pi$). In other words, if we measure the energy of a quantum particle very precisely, then there would be an inherent uncertainty in time at which the energy measurement had been made and the product of these two uncertainties is going to be higher than the Planck constant, $h/2\pi$. This uncertainty principle is the bedrock of quantum mechanics. It has been proven time and time again that this uncertainty principle is inviolable and holds true in all quantum events. Heisenberg received the Nobel Prize in Physics in 1932 for this contribution to quantum mechanics.

In the sub-atomic world of quantum mechanics, there may be a situation which is known as quantum fluctuation. In an otherwise complete vacuum (having nothing), a quantum fluctuation can produce an amount of energy (known as vacuum energy) and that energy can generate a virtual electron-positron pair in the system. Now that energy comes from nature, as if nature is lending that energy to the system. When the electron-positron pair comes in contact with each other in future, both of them disappear instantly and an amount of energy is produced that is exactly equal to the energy that produced the pair in the first place and that energy is returned to nature and everything is squared up.

This borrowing of energy from nature to form an electron-positron pair (or for that matter matter-antimatter formation) and then annihilation and returning the energy to nature are taking place all the time everywhere, even in a vacuum where we consider there is absolutely nothing. These are the quantum fluctuations. These are not mad physics professors' or mad scientists' brainwaves, these are actual physical phenomena, which have been demonstrated in high-energy physics laboratories. If one measures the charge of an electron with high precision, one can then find a sudden fluctuation in its charge or a slight wobble in the trajectory of the electron. This is due to the interaction of the real electron and the momentary appearance of the electron-positron pair in the vicinity.

Billions and trillions of matter-antimatter particles are popping up and being annihilated all the time everywhere in space. Now a situation may arise when a small fraction of these particles is not annihilated instantaneously and these matter, anti-matter particles move away from each other. In fact, it had been estimated that approximately one in a billion of such pairs had escaped annihilation and moved away to lead separate lives at the time of the Big Bang. Electrons and other matters (atoms) in our everyday world (called *fermions*) came out and formed our world or the present universe, and the positrons and other anti-matter particles formed the anti-matter world somewhere far away from our matter world, or they may have formed a separate anti-matter universe.

Our matter universe and the anti-matter universe are blood enemies. Should they come in contact, they will annihilate each other instantly and an unimaginable release of energy will take place. However, this energy is what these matter and anti-matter universes owe to nature, because this energy was borrowed at the time of forming matter and anti-matter particles in a gigantic scale. Whereas all the other particles returned their energies to nature, these particles, statistically one in a billion particles, escaped repayment and formed the universe.

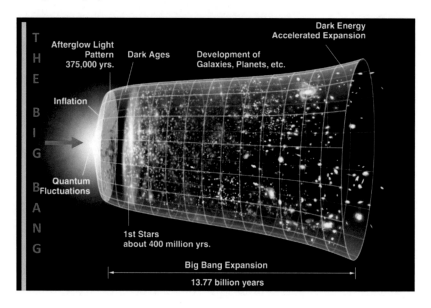

Figure 1.11   The Big Bang arising from quantum fluctuations (courtesy NASA)

This is how the universe, as perceived now, came into existence. It is the formation of the universe out of nothing and the likely disappearance of the universe to nothing. There is no need to invent a divine power and then lay everything at the feet of that invented divine power. In fact, such an invention, all within the confines of our minds, would create more insurmountable problems in explaining things as they stand – such as where is the divine power now, how did He create these things, did He create the universe on a whim or did He have an ultimate purpose etc.?

Albert Einstein was deeply sceptical about the divine power. He expressed his thought quite bluntly in saying, *"I want to know how God created this world. I am not interested in this or that phenomenon, in the spectrum of this or that element. I want to know His thoughts; the rest are details."*

It must be stated that the present perception of the creation of the universe is not a done deal. The debate about the universe, its progression, its ultimate fate etc., are all raging in the scientific community now. This is the credit for science – science never claims to have reached the goal or achieved the ultimate truth; anything that is held to be true now can be changed in the light of new evidence and new facts in the future. This is in stark contrast with religion where everything is claimed to have come from God or Allah and hence is not subject to any alteration or modification. This is what science rejects.

Is a black hole a black mystery?

A black hole – hitherto an invisible celestial body - was in cosmological vocabulary even before Einstein's general theory of relativity in 1916. It was a mystical entity, to say the least. But when the general theory of relativity predicted with full scientific rigour that a massive stellar body can have such a strong gravitational pull (due to warping of space) that nothing, no object, not even electromagnetic radiation such as light can escape it, the general idea of a black hole became firmly established in technical minds. But it remained only a technical curiosity at that time as no scientific evidence or mechanism for the formation of a black hole was put forward. While Einstein's theory predicted the existence of black holes, he himself did not believe that they existed.

In 1930, during a long voyage to London to study physics at Cambridge university, a 19-year-old Indian astrophysicist, Subrahmanyan Chandrasekhar, showed via calculations that when a massive star runs out of nuclear fuel, it would blow itself apart in a spectacularly violent explosion and turn into a black hole, only when the original mass of the star was larger than 1.4 times the mass of the Sun. On arrival at Cambridge, he showed his work to his assigned supervisor. But his supervisor reprimanded him for holding crazy ideas and told him to get down to work at Cambridge. Chandrasekhar could not pursue his research on black holes, but his work subsequently received great admiration in cosmology and the term 'Chandrasekhar's limit' came into technical vocabulary. He received the Nobel Prize in 1983, not for his work on black holes, but for *"studies of the physical processes of importance to the structure and evolution of the stars."*

Sir Roger Penrose of Oxford University proved mathematically in 1965 that black holes are natural consequences of the theory of relativity. However, a German physicist, Karl

Schwarzschild provided the proof of their existence just less than two months after Einstein published the general relativity equations in 1916. By solving the equations exactly, he identified a radius, known as the Schwarzschild radius, that defines the horizon or boundary of a voracious gravitational sinkhole. If a massive object could be compressed to fit within the Schwarzschild radius, which is three kilometres per solar mass, no known force could stop it from collapsing into the sinkhole and that sinkhole is the black hole. But that solution was so revolutionary at the time that it was ignored by the physics establishment. Moreover, there was no faint evidence that anything like black holes ever existed.

But a black hole became a realistic possibility after the detection of pulsars some decades later. The detection of *pulsars* (pulsating neutron stars) by Jocelyn Bell Burnell, a research student at the University of Cambridge in 1967, gave a renewed spurt to the concept of gravitational collapse and the formation of black holes. A normal star, when it comes to the end of its life due to lack of nuclear fusion fuel, collapses under its own gravity and becomes a neutron star. It may be mentioned that an atom consists of neutrons (neutral in charge) and positively charged protons and negatively charged electrons. If gravity becomes too strong, protons and electrons are pulled together to merge with each other, neutralise their charges and become neutrons and the whole star becomes a neutron star. For the detection of the neutron star, which was considered *"one of the most significant scientific achievements of the 20th century"* by the Nobel Committee, her supervisor and another astronomer were awarded the Nobel prize in Physics in 1974, but Jocelyn Bell was not even mentioned in the citation. However, years later, in 2018, she was awarded the Special Breakthrough Prize in Fundamental Physics. She donated the entire amount of prize money of £2.3 million to the Institute of Physics in the UK to help female, minority, and refugee students become physics researchers. What a generosity by a woman who had been so unfairly removed from the award of the Nobel Prize she deserved most!

Not all stars eventually become neutron stars. If the mass of a star is less than 1.4 times the mass of the Sun, the gravity would not be strong enough to turn it into a neutron star. If the mass is greater than 1.4 times the mass of the Sun, the outcome is a neutron star. The gravitational pull in a neutron star ultimately becomes so strong that all its mass and its nearby matters are pulled to a small volume and the star becomes a black hole. A black hole can merge with another black hole to become a bigger and stronger black hole.

It is speculated that there are black holes of various sizes in most of the galaxies and in some galaxies, there are supermassive black holes at their centres. The nearest black holes to Earth are quite a few thousand light-years away; but they are not large enough to exert any influence on this planet. The supermassive black hole in our galaxy (the Milky Way) is about 26,000 light-years away.

Despite the name, a black hole is not all black. The gas and dust trapped around the edges of the black hole are compacted so densely and heated up so enormously that there are literally gigantic cauldrons of fire around the periphery of a black hole. The temperatures can be around billions of degrees!

The first direct visual evidence of a black hole was produced on 10 April 2019 by a team of over 200 international experts working in a number of countries. The Event Horizon Telescope (EHT) was used to detect the existence of a colossal black hole in the M87 galaxy, in the Virgo galaxy cluster. The computer simulation from data collected in the EHT is shown in Figure 1.12 below. This black hole is located some 55 million light-years from the Earth and its estimated mass is 6.5 billion times that of the Sun! So, this black hole is truly a monster of a black hole.

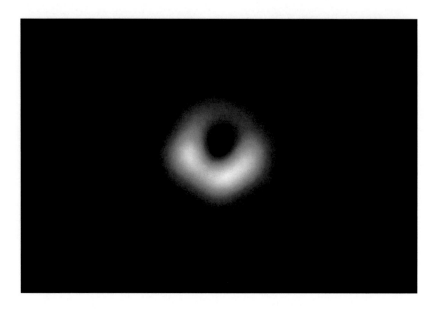

Figure 1.12.   Computer simulation of a black hole from real data

Although it is a ginormous black hole, its size is quite small and it is incredibly far away (520 million, million, million kilometres away) from Earth. To observe directly that elusive black hole, astronomers require a telescope with an angular resolution so sharp that it would be like spotting an apple on the surface of the Moon from Earth and the aerial dish that would be required for such a detection would be around the size of the Earth! Obviously, that is not practical.

Instead, an international team of experts devised a Very Long Baseline Interferometry (VLBI) technique, which involves picking up radio signals (wavelength 1.3 mm) by a network of radio telescopes scattered around the globe. The locations of these radio telescopes, eight in number, are shown in Figure 1.13 below. When radio signals from these radio-telescopes are collected and joined up, taking into account their geographical locations, lapsed times for signal detection etc., and processed in a supercomputer, an image was gradually built up of the bright part of the periphery of the black hole.

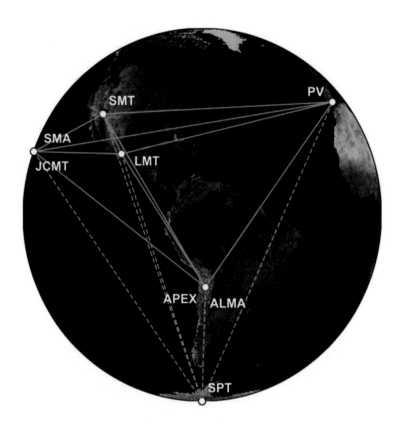

Figure 1.13.   Locations of Event Horizon Telescopes (EHT)

The key feature of a black hole is its event horizon – the boundary at which even light cannot escape its gravitational pull. The size of the event horizon depends on the mass of the black hole. Once an object crosses the boundary of the event horizon, there is absolutely no chance of coming back. A lead astronomer from MIT working on this EHT team said, *"a black hole is a one-way door out of this Universe."*

The general theory of relativity also predicts that a black hole will have a 'shadow' around it which may be around three times larger than the event horizon size. This shadow is caused by gravitational bending of light by the black hole. If something gets nearer the shadow, it can possibly escape the gravitational pull of the black hole, if its speed is sufficiently high (comparable to the speed of light).

It is postulated that the shadow comprises a number of rings around the event horizon. The nearer a ring is to the event horizon, the more rigorous and compact it is with extreme pressure-temperature conditions.

If, for example, an unfortunate human being falls even into the outer ring of the shadow, they will be pulled towards the black hole initially slowly and then progressively strongly – their legs will be pulled more vigorously than their upper part and gradually their body will be stretched into a long thin strip like spaghetti. And when that spaghetti shape crosses the event horizon, it will be stretched so much that it will become a very thin and very long string of atoms!

Figure 1.14.   Is a wormhole a link between a black hole and a white hole?

The general perception of a black hole is that it is a monstrous vacuum cleaner where everything, even light, is sucked up through a funnel and nothing, absolutely nothing, can come out. It absorbs an enormous amount of matter and squashes it into tiny volumes. What happens to this gigantic amount of matter is a mystery, a black mystery.

There are two parallel streams of purely speculative thoughts. One is that when a black hole becomes too big - either by incessantly swallowing up matters from its surroundings or by merging with other black holes – a super-giant explosion, more like a Big Bang, may take place. So, a black hole may be the mother of a new Big Bang, a new generation of the universe.

The other thought is that the funnel of a black hole is connected through a neck, called a *wormhole*, to a different space-time and hence a different universe at the other end, as shown in Figure 1.14. All the materials that a black hole sucks up at the front end in this universe go through the wormhole to another reverse funnel where all the materials are spewed out into a different space-time. That funnel is called the white hole. Thus, a black hole and a white hole are a conjugate pair - a connection between two universes! But the question is, since there are billions of black holes in our universe, then there could be billions of corresponding wormholes and white holes and universes.

Two super-massive black holes or a series of black holes in the galaxy cluster called Ophiuchus (pronounced as Ophioukhos) have recently been detected to have merged over an area bigger than that of our own galaxy, the Milky Way! This Ophiuchus is a large constellation of galaxies straddling the celestial equator. The merging of black holes took place some 390 million light years from the Earth.

Gravitational waves

Gravitational waves, space-time deformation, quantum gravity etc., are now the buzz words in scientific as well as non-scientific parlance. People tend to show off their academic excellence by frequently and, often inappropriately, using these terms and dazzling their audience, but now they can have some inkling of the implications of these terms. These terms ushered in a new frontier of scientific knowledge in the general area of cosmology. A new scientific toolkit has been invented for the cosmologists and astrophysicists to use.

If the early part of the 20th century could be categorised as the age of the theory of relativity (advanced by Einstein in 1905 and in 1915-1916) and then the age of quantum mechanics (advanced by Max Planck, Albert Einstein, Niels Bohr, Heisenberg, Schrodinger and others), then this part of the 21st century can surely be described as the age of gravitational waves.

But the recent detection of gravitational waves was not a fortuitous event. Back in 1916, when Einstein produced the general theory of relativity, he stipulated the space-time continuum. But nobody, except a very few elites in theoretical physics, had the faintest idea what it really meant.

According to *the general theory of relativity*, gravity is a manifestation of the curvature of the space-time continuum. The space-time becomes curved, and time slows down in the presence of the material body. The more the mass, the greater the curvature and the slower the time. When a massive body moves, the curvature moves with it to a new position stretching the space in one direction and compressing it in another. This deformation in space-time produces ripples, called gravitational waves, which travel outward from the gravitational source at the speed of light. But there is no light involved, only gravitational energy travels at the speed of light.

In a more mundane way one can say that when a body is attracted and moves towards another body, it follows the curved space-time fabric. When there are a number of bodies, the space-time curvature becomes quite jagged and a body travelling in that space follows a tortuous path.

It may, however, be mentioned here that there is no scientific reason why bodies should always attract each other, as they do in our observable universe. In another parallel universe, it may be that bodies repel each other, or some bodies repel while others attract. When these attracting and repelling bodies are scattered randomly in the vast space, they may stabilise and create a stable universe - all attracting bodies may not collapse and all repelling bodies may not push each other into infinity. For example, our universe of bodies attracting each other does not collapse into a single body.

How does this gravitational attraction get propagated between the bodies? Drawing an analogy between the electromagnetic energy and gravitational energy, physicists coined the term *'graviton'* for gravitational energy, as *'photon'* is for electromagnetic energy. The photon is the smallest packet of energy (the quantum of energy) that came into the jargon of physics following Einstein's theory of photoelectric effect in 1905. It may be mentioned that Einstein received the Nobel prize for his theory of photoelectric effect, not for the theory of relativity, although both theories are of immense importance in physical sciences.

Whereas the photon had been detected experimentally, the graviton had never been detected. How was, despite all the predictions of the general theory of relativity being found to be meticulously accurate, the central plank of this theory involving gravitational waves left undetected? That gap has now been filled. This recent discovery of gravitational waves may eventually lead to the identification of the graviton. But whether or not the graviton comes into the scientific arena, the gravitational wave is now a reality.

When the *LIGO* (Laser Interferometer Gravitational-wave Observatory) collaborative experiments in Baton Rouge, Louisiana and in Hanford, Washington State first detected the gravitational wave, they hesitated to make it public. It was so earth-shattering that the researchers had to make it absolutely certain that the results were genuine, not spurious. After all, no scientist wants egg on their face! On September 14th 2015, they disclosed the detection of gravitational waves – exactly 100 years after Einstein's prediction.

When two super-massive black holes some 1.3 billion light years away, one 36 times and the other 29 times the mass of the Sun, spiralled around each another and eventually merged, a gigantic, massive black hole was created. And, in the final half a second or so in this cataclysmic event, a massive amount of energy in the form of gravitational energy was produced. It had been estimated that the final black hole, instead of having 65 times the mass of the Sun was 62 times and the remaining three solar masses had been converted to gravitational energy. This energy was so massive that it rippled through the whole universe at the speed of light and deformed the space-time fabric by gravitational waves. It may be noted that there was no emission of light at all from the collapse of those spiralling black holes – the energy was all gravitational energy. The generated energy from the conversion of three solar masses (each having a mass of 2×10^{30}kg) was absolutely staggering ($\sim 5 \times 10^{47}$ J).

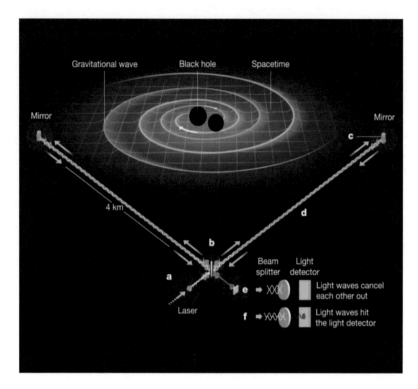

Figure 1.15 Detection of gravitational waves (courtesy of Nature 469, Vol 568, 25 April 2019). Image credit: ©Johan Jarnestad/The Royal Swedish Academy of Sciences

At the LIGO facility, a monochromatic laser beam was produced and then split in two directions at the point of origin. The facility comprised two arms at right angles to each other and each arm was 4km long through which the laser beams travelled. At the edge of these arms, precisely positioned reflecting mirrors were placed. The reflected beams were allowed to interfere back at the source. If there was no space distortion due to ripples in the space-time, the reflected beams combining in anti-phases would cancel each other and there would be no interference pattern. On the other hand, if the arms of the facility were deformed due to stretching and compression by the incoming gravitational wave, there would be interference. This physical deformation was extremely small – a trillion times smaller than the width of a human hair (~10^{-18}m) – and even with the emission of an astounding amount of energy (~5×10^{47}J), an extreme precision in detection by laser interferometer was needed.

Since that detection in 2015, more black hole mergers of smaller sizes were detected. That shows that the technique is becoming more refined and sensitive. Even smaller masses than black holes can create ripples in gravitational waves, and they may be detected by this technique. In September 2017, LIGO had been closed for about a year for an upgrade. But before shutdown, on August 17, 2017, LIGO detected gravitational waves produced by the collision of two neutron stars in the galaxy Hydra, 130 million light years away. This is the first time that collision between stars had been detected. In August, a new facility in Italy, called the Virgo interferometer, had joined in. India is also going to build a facility in Maharashtra, which is similar to the LIGO facility in Washington State and plans to start its operation in 2024.

This gravitational wave may be a cosmic messenger which could lead human beings to probe right into the origin of the universe. This is an exciting time not only for cosmologists and astrophysicists, but also for humanity as a whole; we will no longer rely on myths and mysteries passed down from generations to generations about the creation of the universe.

Dark matter and dark energy - Part I

Until about 100 years ago, the prevailing scientific perception was that our universe was eternal, invariant and in quiescent state. But science has progressed tremendously since then and the very perception of Universe had changed significantly. Albert Einstein's general theory of relativity in 1916 had revolutionised our view of spacetime of the Universe. Following the general theory of relativity, the Russian physicist Alexander Friedmann in 1922 as well as Belgian astronomer Georges Lemaitre in 1927, independently produced solutions to Einstein's field equations to show that Universe is actually expanding.

The planet Earth is one of the eight planets orbiting the Sun. The Sun has curbed out a region of space in the sky where its influence is most dominant and that is called the Heliosphere, as shown in Figure 1.16. This Sun provides us on this planet Earth with all the energy we need to live and flourish. The distance between the Sun and the Earth is known as one Astronomical Unit (AU) and it is estimated that the gravitational field of the Solar system fades away at about 100,000 AU (~1.58 light years).

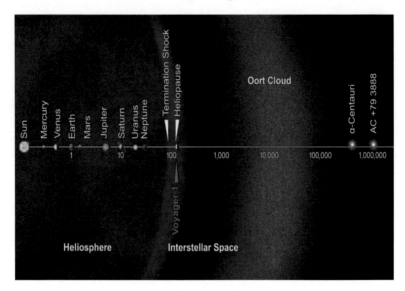

Figure 1.16   The Solar System

The Sun may seem overpowering to us and indeed it is, but in the wider perspective the Sun is just an average or below average star in our galaxy, the Milky Way. It is estimated that there are around 300 billion stars, yes, 300,000,000,000 stars in an average galaxy and our galaxy is no more than an average galaxy. In a galaxy there are lots of other celestial bodies such as white dwarfs, neutron stars, supernovae, pulsars (pulsating stars), black holes and many more. Our spiral galaxy, the Milky Way, is about 100,000 light years (ly) across, which means that travelling at the speed of light (300,000 km per second) it will take 100,000 years to go from one end of this galaxy to the other end. One may consider that the speed of light is such that it would go round the Earth seven and half times every second! Our nearest galaxy is Andromeda, which is roughly 2.5 million light years away from us and that galaxy is about 220,000 ly across. It is estimated that there are over 100 billion galaxies in the Universe! So, altogether there would be 30 billion trillion stars (like our Sun) in the

Universe (=300 billion stars per galaxy x 100 billion galaxies). The extent of the observable Universe is estimated to be about 93 billion light years across following the Wilkinson Microwave Anisotropy Probe (WMAP). Now you have a feel of the enormity of the Universe! An image of the observable Universe is shown in Figure 1.17.

Figure 1.17   WMAP-2010 image of the observable Universe

In 1915-16 when Albert Einstein produced the general theory of relativity, his field equations predicted that the Universe was expanding. But the prevailing scientific perception (as well as theological dictum) was that the Universe was static and in steady state. So, in 1917, he introduced arbitrarily (against the grain of the field equations) a quantity called the cosmological constant, Λ, with a particular value which would block out the expansion of the Universe. The cosmological constant is the energy density of space or vacuum energy. But in 1929 the American astronomer, Edwin Hubble, made astronomical observations of distant galaxies that showed redshifts, which was evidence that the Universe was actually expanding, not static. That redshift was shown to be proportional to the distance of that galaxy from Earth (linear redshift-distance relationship). It turned the whole of prevailing wisdom on its head and Einstein was left deeply embarrassed. He humbly admitted that the introduction of the cosmological constant was the 'biggest blunder' of his life. Without this constraining factor, the equations would naturally lead to predictions of an *expanding Universe*.

The general theory of relativity produced the space-time continuum. There is no gravitational force of attraction in the conventional sense. The gravitational field is the space. The gravity creates a curvature in space, more like a heavy body when placed in a trampoline would create a dent, which other lighter bodies would roll down in particular trajectories and that is the analogy of gravitational attraction. Within about two months of publication of the general theory of relativity, the German physicist Karl Schwarzschild provided the proof of existence of gravitational sinkholes, now called black holes, in the Universe. By solving the field equations, he produced a radius, now called the Schwarzschild radius, that defines the boundary of a black hole. A black hole curves the space towards itself so sharply that nothing, not even light, can escape it once it is within the grip of the black hole and that is why this body is termed as a black hole.

As mentioned above, the Universe is truly unimaginably large. The visible part of the Universe contains celestial bodies that are made up of ordinary baryonic matter such as protons and neutrons, and non-baryonic matter such as electrons, neutrinos etc. For each one of these ordinary matters, there are corresponding anti-matters. For example, there are anti-protons, anti-neutrons, anti-electrons etc. The sinister attribute of these ordinary matters and anti-matters is that when they happen to come in contact with each other, they annihilate each other in a flash and an equivalent amount of energy is created as per

Einstein's mass-energy equivalence equation. Since we are in this ordinary world, there may be an anti-world somewhere, made up of anti-matter. But we must never meet each other. If we do, we will end up in a flash into an enormous bundle of energy – creating billions and trillions of times more energy than the Sun.

In our visible Universe containing billions of galaxies and each galaxy containing billions of stars, it is estimated that there are also a large number of black holes hidden in each galaxy. Black holes exert a tremendous amount of gravitational pull to keep billions of stars within the galaxy together. But there is a physical dilemma. If black holes are situated nearer the central core of the galaxy where most of the turbulent celestial activities are taking place, then what is keeping the outlying stars in place where the gravitational pull is much weaker? Still, it has been found that even the remotest of the stars have the same orbital motion as the ones nearer the centre. How do those stars get sufficient gravitational pull to have same orbital motions? To resolve this dilemma, astrophysicists and cosmologists came up with the solution that there must be large amounts of unseen matter dotted all over the galaxies which exert gravitational pull to the stars to have similar orbital motion! This unseen matter is called dark matter.

There are similarities and dissimilarities between ordinary matter and dark matter. Whereas ordinary matter interacts with light, or generally speaking with electromagnetic energies, dark matter does not. Light goes straight through dark matter. But it has gravitational pull exactly like ordinary matter. Although unseen by modern scientific devices, dark matter can be detected by its gravitational fingerprint. Dark matter keeps the fabric of the galaxy intact.

What is this dark matter and what are its constituents? Modern physics has no clue. It cannot be made up of baryonic matters, meaning ordinary protons and neutrons. If they were, they would react to light energy, but they do not. It is speculated that it could be made up of esoteric constituents such as axions,

Weakly Interacting Massive Particles (WIMPs), Gravitationally Interacting Massive Particles (GIMPs), supersymmetric particles etc. These are pure speculations. Also, as dark matter and dark energy together comprise 95.5 per cent of the Universe's all mass-energy composition, they may be coupled or tangled quantum mechanically!

The next article will deal with dark energy and why dark energy is needed to have the expansion and accelerated expansion of the Universe that is taking place at the moment. In fact, without dark energy, the Universe might have collapsed under its own gravitational pull or might not even have come into existence in the first place.

Dark matter and dark energy – Part II

In the first part on this topic the essential attributes of dark matter were described. Dark matter was necessary in order to hold the basic fabric of galaxies together; otherwise, billions of stars at the edges of the galaxies would experience weaker gravitational pull and could even fall away from the galactic orbits. So, dark matters were invoked to be present all over the galactic system. In this part, the role of the dark energy will be considered. Dark matter may keep the individual galactic system intact and maintain higher orbital speeds to outlying stars, but then what is giving the Universe the impetus to expand?

The 'Standard Model' of the cosmological system predicted that the Universe simply could not exist in a quiescent steady state – it has to be dynamic in nature, meaning it either has to expand or contract. Indeed, in 1929, Edwin Hubble made an astronomical observation and that became incontrovertible showing that the Universe was actually expanding. That made Einstein admit that his cosmological constant, Λ (lambda) introduced in the general theory of relativity with a particular value to force a steady state condition for the Universe was flawed. For the next 70 years, until 1998, cosmologists implicitly took Λ to be zero and the Universe was described as per Einstein's field equations. Nobody thought of discarding the cosmological constant that Einstein had introduced, albeit mistakenly.

Then in 1998, another even more astounding evidence was produced based on observation using the Hubble telescope, when it was shown that light from very distant supernovae was fading away and showing redshifts indicating that supernovae were receding, and were receding at faster rates the further they were from the Earth. In other words, there was an accelerated expansion in the Universe. The Universe's current expansion rate is known as the Hubble constant, H_0 which is estimated to be approximately 73.5 km per second per megaparsec. A megaparsec is the distance of 3.26 million light years. As the speed of light is 3×10^8 m/s or 9.46×10^{12} km/year, 1 megaparsec then equals to 3.08×10^{19} km. A galaxy 1 megaparsec away (3.08×10^{19} km) would recede from Earth at 73.5 km/s, whereas another galaxy 10 times of 1 megaparsec from the Earth would recede at 10 times of 73.5 km per sec = 735 km per sec. That was a shocking result, and the cosmologists were taken completely by surprise.

What is providing this gigantic Universe with enough energy to expand and expand at an accelerated rate? Further observations had demonstrated that this accelerated expansion is in fact taking place in the vast extra-galactic spaces. This came to be known as the 'metric expansion'. There was no evidence or verifiable evidence of expansion within the individual territories of galaxies. It may indeed be argued that if there were any expansion within a galactic system, then stars would move away from each other and even the planets revolving round the stars would recede. For example, Earth would recede from the Sun and that recessive path would look like a spiral trajectory and eventually Earth would secede completely from the Heliosphere! This would be a recipe for a total disaster for the Earth-bound lives like ours and luckily there was no such evidence of recession.

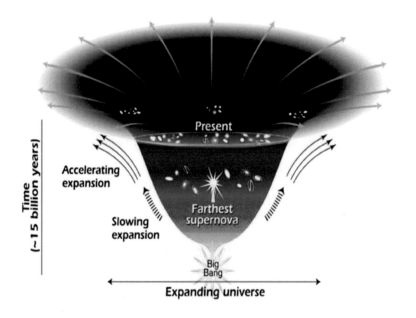

Figure 1.18   Accelerated expansion of the Universe

Albert Einstein's *cosmological constant,* Λ in the general theory of relativity came to the rescue of the paradox of cosmological expansion. Dark energy was invoked to solve this problem. Dark energy is perceived as the intrinsic energy of the empty space or simply the vacuum energy. It may be pointed out that space is viewed as the gravitational field. As there are limitless empty spaces in the cosmological scale, dark energy can also be limitless. Although the precise mechanism of the generation of dark energy is unknown, some of the essential characteristics may be drawn. Dark energy is repulsive in character. Thus, dark energy can be viewed as something that reacts with ordinary matter (baryonic matter) making up the celestial bodies, but in the opposite direction to ordinary gravity. Some scientists speculate that dark energy may even be form of a new type of force - the fifth force - which is as yet unknown.

63

The known four forces are: electromagnetic force, weak nuclear force, strong nuclear force and the gravitational force and the properties of these forces are well known. If indeed the fifth force does come into play, it would offer a situation where gravity and anti-gravity may come to exist in the same Universe. It may be that the attractive gravity exists within the scale of galaxies, whereas repulsive gravity exists in the vast extra-galactic space!

Taking material accounting of galaxies and their physical characteristics that are evident from astronomical observations, it is estimated on the basis of mass-energy composition, that the Universe is only 4.5% of ordinary matter, 26.1% of dark matter and 69.4% of dark energy. However, this distribution of mass-energy composition in observable celestial bodies and unobservable black holes does not remain fixed or invariant. At the early part of the Universe's formation, after about 380,000 years following the Big Bang (~13.8 billion years ago), the distribution mass and energy was quite different. Ordinary matter was 12% and dark matter was 63% and there was no dark energy, as shown in Table 1 below. The situation is quite different now and this shows that the Universe is changing, or one can say evolving.

Table 1   *The Universe's mass-energy composition*

	13.8 billion years ago	Present day (2000 CE)
Dark energy	-	69.4%
Photons	15%	-
Ordinary matter	12%	4.5%
Neutrinos	10%	-
Dark matter	63.0%	26.1%

In the Universe, as ordinary matter (baryonic matter) is fixed and as the Universe expands, the average density of ordinary matter is continuously diminishing, as density is the amount of material divided by the volume. Similarly, the dark matter density of the Universe also is also decreasing as the Universe expands. But the dark energy density has been found to remain constant, no matter how much or how fast the Universe expands. It is due to the fact that vacuum energy is constantly added (as space has intrinsic vacuum energy) to the pool of dark energy as the Universe expands and hence the dark energy density remains constant.

In the metric expansion, the space or more appropriately, space-time fabric is created extra-galactic. Space is not something which is devoid of other things. Space is the gravitational field. Like the electromagnetic field, the gravitational field generating space is granular in character. The quanta of space are so incredibly small that that we do not feel them, similar to solid granular atoms we cannot feel. Space granules are literally trillions of times smaller than atoms. Space granules or space quanta are not within the space, space quanta are the space. A new branch of physics, called 'loop quantum gravity' shows how space quanta make up the space. When the Universe expands, space is produced with space-time quanta and the intrinsic dark energies increase.

Although the evidence of accelerated expansion of the Universe was baffling, it was nothing unexpected. The Universe had undergone very rapid expansion at the early phase of its existence, some 13.8 billion years ago, after that it slowed down for billions of years and then the expansion phase started about four or five billion years ago. When this expansion will come to a stop or even reverse, nobody knows. But it is definite that the Universe as a whole is not static, it is very much dynamic, vibrant and evolving. If anybody says that the Earth, Sun and Moon and even the whole Universe were created by some unknown Creator and then he left the whole thing in a quiescent state, then there is every reason to reason to question such unfounded claims and discard them as totally baseless.

Are we heading towards genetic disaster?

Lives on Earth in various forms and shapes have come about through very complex and convoluted processes. Single cell organisms like *amoebae* to multi-cellular organisms of plants and animals have progressed through millions of years of slow and painstaking developments of trials and errors, alterations, modifications and so forth, which have collectively come to be called the evolutionary process. Eventually, when an organism emerges in some viable form, it is not the end of the process, it is only the beginning. It will go on for further refinement to a better, fitter, form of life. It may, nonetheless, take a wrong evolutionary turn and suffer the wrath of nature and become extinct. For every surviving form of life, there are tens or even hundreds of similar lives that have either failed to develop properly to be fit for purpose and hence have gone extinct.

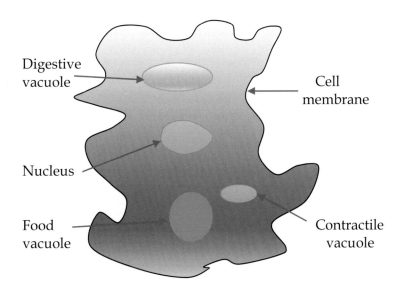

Figure 1.19   *The structure of an amoeba*

Life, particularly human life, comes into existence in a tortuous way. When a male sperm cell fertilises a female egg cell (also called an ovum cell), the combined single cell, called the zygote, is formed. The sperm cell produced in the testes of the male and the egg cell produced in the ovary of the female are the reproductive organ cells - each contains 23 chromosomes – and when they combine, they make up a fully developed cell containing 46 chromosomes. It may be noted that not all sperm cells fertilise egg cells. The reproductive cells must meet at the right time to be fertilised and produce the zygote, which becomes the cell of the new individual. This single cell zygote keeps dividing by a process called cell division, as it moves along the Fallopian tube towards the uterus. The zygote contains all the genetic instructions inherited from the father and the mother. When it reaches the uterus in three to five days, the zygote becomes what is called a blastocyst or a ball of cells. The blastocyst consists of two parts: an outer cell mass that becomes part of the placenta and an inner cell mass that becomes the human body.

A cell is the basic, functional unit of life. A cell is surrounded by a cell membrane and within the membrane lies a blob· of transparent dilute fluid, called cytoplasm, and within the cytoplasm lies the cell nucleus. The nucleus of human cells contains 46 chromosomes in 23 pairs. A chromosome consists of a very long *DNA* helix in which thousands of *genes* are embedded. It is claimed that the secrets of life are all incorporated within these DNA molecules. The discovery of this secret is a fascinating story.

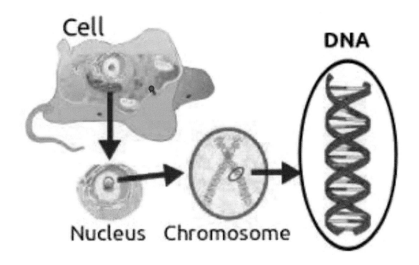

Figure 1.20   Cell structure with cell composition

In the early 1940s, the Austrian physicist Erwin Schrodinger, one of the pioneers of quantum physics, wrote a very thoughtful science classics book called *What is Life?* He maintained that there was no divine power or mysterious spirit that needed to animate life. He speculated that the life force must come from within the body, probably embedded within the molecules of the body. Inspired by Schrodinger's book, physicist Francis Crick teamed up with geneticist James Watson and Maurice Wilkins to study molecular biology and eventually discovered the structure of the DNA molecule within the cell. The trio won the Nobel Prize for Physiology or Medicine in 1962 for their discoveries concerning the "molecular structure of nucleic acids and its significance in information transfer in living material".

They discovered that the DNA molecule has a double helix structure. A gene is a small segment of a DNA molecule, or one segment of a DNA may contribute to more than one gene. A gene embodies an individual functional unit in the biological system which effectively contains the information needed to make molecules called proteins. The production of proteins from a gene's encoded instructions is quite a complex process. First of all, the double helix DNA is unzipped, a small section at a time, and transcribed into single stranded *RNA* (Ribo Nucleic Acid) which contains instructions to generate a protein of a particular type. This type of RNA is called the messenger RNA (mRNA). The mRNA then moves out of the cell nucleus and interacts with a ribosome in the cytoplasm. The ribosome 'reads' the message to produce particular types of amino acid. Amino acids are the building blocks of proteins. This transfer RNA (tRNA) then assembles the protein.

Thus, the cells with all the internal complexities and functions constitute the smallest unit of life. There are multitudes of cell types, but the basic structure is the same. The blastocyst, formed out of zygotes, contains *embryonic stem cells*. It is estimated that humans contain 40 trillion (40,000 billion) cells in a fully developed body.

The embryonic stem cells are extremely important as they contain all the genetic information of an individual, unmodified and unaltered. These embryonic stem cells are pluripotent stem cells, meaning they can divide into more stem cells or can change into any type of tissue cell, such as a blood cell, liver cell, skin cell, brain cell etc. Because of this ability and their unaltered state, embryonic stem cells are highly prized for medical research. But there are downsides too; the embryo has to be sacrificed to extract these cells and that raises serious ethical objections.

When embryonic stem cells mature, they become tissue-specific somatic cells tasked to produce body tissues and there are more than 200 types of tissue cells in the body. Each of these cells contains the full genetic code, no matter where it finds itself, although all instructions to divide and grow are suppressed, except for this particular tissue. For example, blood cells are only responsible for generating blood, liver cells for the liver, skin cells for the skin etc., although each one has the full blueprint for life. There are also non-embryonic stem cells, namely adult stem cells or induced pluripotent stem cells.

Medical research is going ahead using stem cells to cure humans from ailments such as strokes, to repair heart muscles following heart attacks, and to cure neurological problems like Alzheimer's disease, Parkinson's disease etc. Stem cells can be used to produce insulin to cure people with diabetes.

Stem cells can also be used to regenerate or repair organs and limbs such as the nose, ears, lungs, arms and legs and so forth. This aspect promises to have tremendous beneficial effects on soldiers who have lost their organs or limbs in battlefields. They can have their limbs repaired genetically or even have them newly grown in the laboratory. These are not pie in the sky aspirations. Already some organs such as hearts or lungs have been developed in the laboratories, but not *in situ* in primates or humans.

With such wide-ranging medical benefits against incurable and debilitating diseases and ailments, why then are Western countries banning or putting restrictions on the use of stem cells and particularly embryonic stem cells in medical research? It is due to the fact that from the cure of these diseases, it is a small step forward to modify the human genome in such a way that artificial superhumans can be produced. In other words, superhuman Frankensteins can be produced with all the attributes one desires. Thus, uncontrolled medical research can lead to eugenics through the back door or make it a distinct possibility.

Before and during the second world war, Hitler and his Nazi party seriously considered developing a super-Euro/Aryan race where people would not only be physically strong and intellectually superior, but also free from all genetic diseases. It may, however, be noted that this idea of eugenics was not invented by the Nazis, it was imported from a Californian company who had been working on it for quite a few years prior to the 1930s.

When cloned humans with edited and vetted genes are produced, what would be the fate of normal human beings born traditionally with male and female fertilisation processes and with normal genetic make-up? Eugenics proposed that all those people who were deemed by the State to be racially inferior such as Jews, gypsies and so forth as well as the disabled and genetically disordered people etc., had to be exterminated to make way for the superior human race! The fact that eugenics died with Hitler was a great blessing for human race.

Stem cell research with the specific purpose of curing diseases such as diabetes, cancer, genetic disorders, neurological diseases like Parkinson's, Alzheimer's, dementia etc., are the beneficial aspects. But this can go a little further and pave the way to dehumanize humans or even destroy humanity. It is a double-edged sword – use it carefully, otherwise risk it to destroy humanity.

The process of cloning stem cells is reasonably straightforward. Initially the cell nucleus (containing the *DNA*) is removed from the egg cell and then a new nucleus to be cloned is inserted into the egg cell. The egg cell then begins to develop into an embryonic stem cell. This embryonic stem cell becomes identical to the donor's cells. This process can be used to produce therapeutic cloning to treat diabetes, Alzheimer's and many more diseases. The skin cell of a patient suffering from Alzheimer's can be used to generate an embryonic stem cell and then inserted into the patient to treat the disease, as the embryonic stem cell becomes any cell in the body.

One thing that this genetic manipulation may do, if allowed to go unchecked, is to make human immortality a reality. Although sheep, cattle etc., have been successfully cloned, primates and human beings have not yet been cloned. It is primarily because the research and *in-situ* testing of cloning on humans is banned almost everywhere in the world. But if that ban is removed, the technology can then be developed fairly quickly.

The implication of human cloning is enormous. A very rich man (or woman) near the end of his (or her) life may decide to live on for ever. Of course, he himself cannot live for ever as he will age, his body functions will deteriorate and his body will gradually decay. But what he can do is to donate his cells, particularly stem cells for future fertilisation. His stem cells may be deep frozen and, as per his instructions, they may be fertilised at the specified time and a human being will come out of the cloning process. That particular (rich) man is thus reborn; one could say he is reincarnated. That rich man can also in his Will transfer all his wealth to the child (yet to be born) and when the cloned child is born, he is as wealthy as his predecessor. The boy will have many, if not all, of the body functions, body characteristics etc., of the donor, but not his memory nor the personal characteristics derived from the memory. In other words, he will have a blank slate of memory or mind. He will have to learn everything afresh, go to school, play games and develop his individuality, but with the exact replica of the body structure of the donor. Thus, this man can replicate himself over and over again and live for ever!

We are now at the threshold of genetic manipulation, for good or for bad. Gone are the days when we had to blindly believe in a fictitious divine authority creating life on Earth (through Adam and Eve) and submit to religious edicts without any right to question. In reality, life evolved from the single cell amoeba to a multi-cellular organism. Now science and technology have progressed sufficiently enough to create and recreate lives with any genetic make-up. But if we allow artificial genetic creation to take over the natural evolutionary process, it may lead to a disaster of unparalleled proportions. We must resist that temptation at all costs.

Glossary of Terms

Amoeba   A unicellular organism which has the ability to alter its shape primarily by extending and retracting pseudopods. These organisms do not form a single taxonomic group, instead they are found in every major lineage of eukaryotic organism. Eukaryotic organisms are those whose cells have a nucleus enclosed within membranes, unlike prokaryotic organisms which have no membrane-bound organelles.

Baryonic matter   Baryonic matter by definition should only include matter that is composed of baryons. A baryon is a class of composite subatomic particle which is *quark*-based and contains an odd number of quarks (at least three). The important baryons are protons and neutrons. However, in astronomy, baryonic matter is used loosely to include protons, neutrons as well as electrons, although electrons are not quark-based. (A proton is made up of two up-quarks and one down-quark, and a neutron is made up of one up-quark and two down-quarks.) The quarks are held together by strong interaction through *gluons*. Electrons, on the other hand, belong to a class of particles called *leptons*, which are not quark-based and have no strong interaction through gluons.

Baryons are the everyday particles in the universe. Nearly 10% of the universe's baryons are inside galaxies, 50 to 60% in the circum-galactic space and the remaining 30 to 40% are in the Warm Hot Intergalactic Medium (WHIM).

Big Bang   The initial event when the quantum fluctuation caused the generation of enormous amounts of elementary particles like quarks, gluons etc., at an infinitesimally small volume called singularity. Those quarks, at infinitely high temperatures, started joining up to form particles and anti-particles which expanded. This was the moment when space and time came into existence.

Big Crunch   The event when everything in the universe will be pulled together into an infinitely small volume called singularity. At the Big Crunch there will no space, no time. It is just the reverse of the Big Bang.

Black body radiation   A black body is a theoretically idealised body that absorbs radiation at all wavelengths in the visible spectrum. It is coloured black because a black body absorbs most of the radiation and does not emit any radiation at room temperature. However, at elevated temperatures, a black body emits radiation with a characteristic wavelength at which the intensity of emission (fluence) peaks at a certain temperature. The higher the temperature, the lower the wavelength of the highest intensity.

Bosons   Bosons are those quantum particles that follow Bose-Einstein statistics. Examples are photons and mesons.

Cosmological constant, Λ   The cosmological constant, Λ, is the energy density of space or vacuum energy in Einstein's field equations of the general theory of relativity. Einstein introduced this concept in 1917 to counterbalance the effects of gravitational attraction and achieve a static universe, which was the prevailing perception at that time. However, Einstein abandoned the concept in 1931 following Hubble's observation of the expanding universe. From the 1930s till the late 1990s, most physicists assumed the cosmological constant to be zero. That view was changed in 1998 when the expansion of the universe was estimated to be accelerating, implying that there is a positive value of Λ.

Dark energy   Dark energy and dark matter were invoked to have material accounting of the universe. The present universe is expanding at an accelerated rate, but what is giving the universe that amount of energy? It is assumed by scientists that this energy may be dark energy, which is, as yet, unseen and unknown.

Dark matter   Weakly Interacting Massive Particles (WIMPs) are thought of as the elementary particles which make up dark matter. They interact with ordinary visible matter only through gravity, not via electromagnetic forces or strong nuclear forces. Most of the matter in the universe is dark matter. It is estimated that as much as 26.1% of all matter is cold dark matter, 69.4% dark energy and only 4.5% is visible baryonic matter.

DNA   Deoxyribonucleic acid is a molecule comprising two long chains of polynuclides coiling around each other to form a double helix with adenine, thymine, guanine and cytosine. DNA carries the genetic instructions for human lives.

Embryonic stem cell   An embryonic stem cell is the original unmodified stem cell formed in the embryo. These stem cells are highly desirable for medical or genetic research. But when embryonic stem cells are extracted from the embryo, the embryo is damaged or destroyed and hence there are strict regulations against destroying the human lives.

Epigenetics   There is an emerging science of epigenetics which deals with the internal processes that genes can be switched on and off in response to instructions from other genes or from environmental factors or physical factors such as stress or dietary habits. This results in some genes going dormant in some generations only to reappear in subsequent ones.

Expanding Universe   The universe's current expansion rate is known as the Hubble constant, H_0 which is taken to be approximately 73.5km per second per megaparsec. A megaparsec is the distance of 3.26 million light years. Knowing the speed of light as 3×10^8m/s or 9.46×10^{12}km/year, 1 megaparsec then equals to 3.08×10^{19}km. If we observe a star at a distance of 10 times of 1 megaparsec from us, we will see that the star is receding from us at a speed of 10 times of 73.5km per sec = 735km per sec.

Fermions   A fermion is any particle that has an odd half-integral *spin* (1/2 or 3/2 and so forth). Quarks and leptons as well as composite materials like protons, neutrons, electrons are fermions. The fermions obey Fermi-Dirac statistics and follow the Pauli Exclusion Principle.

Forces of nature   There are four fundamental forces of nature and these are: (i) gravitational force, (ii) electromagnetic force, (iii) weak nuclear force and (iv) strong nuclear force.

General theory of relativity   Although Einstein published four separate papers on general relativity in November 1915, he published the final consolidation of various papers on the subject in *Annalen der Physik* in 1916 and that is taken as the paper on the 'General Theory of Relativity'.

Genes   A gene is a sequence of nucleotide in a DNA or RNA molecule that encodes the synthesis of a specific biological function. The inherited attributes are embedded in genes.

Gluons   The strong nuclear force that holds quarks together in the proton and neutron is the force-carrying particle called a gluon. The gluon has a spin of 1. The gluon can interact with itself and with quarks. The gluons always bind particles together so that there is no colour. In other words, red, green and blue quarks join with gluons so that they do not have a colour.

Graviton   The graviton is the quantum of gravity, just like the photon is the quantum of the electromagnetic field. However, the quantum field theory has not yet been developed like the electromagnetic field theory to positively characterise a graviton. But it is assumed that a graviton is the quantum of field that mediates in the gravitational force.

Hadrons   Hadrons are composite particles such as protons, neutrons and mesons comprising quarks and anti-quarks bound together by gluons. A proton has two up-quarks and one down-quark, whereas a neutron is made up of one up-quark and two down-quarks.

Heisenberg uncertainty principle   In quantum mechanics, there is a limit to the precision of a pair of variables such as the position and momentum (Δx and Δp) of a particle or energy and time, (ΔE and Δt) of a particle that can be measured. The precision cannot be better than the uncertainty amount of Planck constant ($h/2\pi$). Heisenberg advanced this principle and hence it is called the Heisenberg uncertainty principle.

Leptons   Leptons (Greek word for 'small mass') are electrons, muon and tau. Leptons are not made up of quarks.

Light year   A light year is the distance that light can travel in one year. The speed of light, c, is 300 million metres per second and so in one year, light travels a distance of 9.5 trillion km. The light from the Sun takes about 8 minutes to come to Earth.

LIGO   Laser Interferometer Gravitational-wave Observatory.

Newton's law of gravity   Newton's law of gravity states that every body attracts every other body with a force proportional to the product of their masses and inversely proportional to the square of their distance. This was the bedrock of classical mechanics.

Momentum   This is the product of mass and velocity of a body.

Photon   Electromagnetic energy is carried by a quantum of energy called photon. It has a spin of 1.

Pulsars   A pulsar (pulsating star) is a highly magnetised rotating neutron star that emits beams of electromagnetic radiation out of its magnetic poles. A pulsar is the remnant of a supernova explosion.

Quasars   A quasar (quasi-stellar source) is a distant galaxy that emits radiation from its central region. The source of radiation is the giant black hole that swallows up material from its surroundings and radiation beyond the event horizon is seen as the glow.

Quarks   Quarks are the constituents of protons and neutrons. The word 'quark' was coined by the Caltech physicist, Murray Gell-Mann almost facetiously when it was discovered. Quarks have six flavours: up, down; strange, charmed; bottom, top. Each flavour comes in three colours: red, green and blue. A proton or a neutron is made up of three quarks, one of each colour, so that the net effect is white. A proton contains two up-quarks and one down-quark; whereas a neutron contains two down-quarks and one up-quark.

RNA   Ribonucleic Acid.

Special theory of relativity This theory produces two fundamental concepts – (i) every motion is relative depending on the position of the observer, but the speed of light is constant (c=3x10^8 m/s), (ii) nothing can travel faster than light.

Spin From the wave-particle duality, everything can be considered as sort of particle. These particles have an inherent property called spin. This spin does not mean that the particle is rotating; rather it tells of the inherent characteristic of the particle. A particle of spin 0 is like a circle, it looks the same from every direction. A particle of spin 1 is like a photo of an object, it looks different from different angles; only when it is rotated the full 360^0, does it look the same. A particle of spin 2 is like a photo of an object and the photocopy of that object stuck upside down together in a page. If one turns the page by 180^0, it looks the same. The force carrying the particle for gravitational force is the graviton and has a spin of 2.

All known particles in the universe can be divided into two groups: one which has spin of ½ and the other of spin 0, 1, 2… The spin ½ particles make up the matter in the universe and are called fermions and they obey Pauli's exclusion principle. The spin 0, 1, 2… makes up the force-carrying particles such as photon (spin: 1); gluon (spin: 1); W$^+$, W$^-$ and Z^0, all spin:1. The graviton has a spin of 2.

Stem cell A stem cell is a special human cell that is able to develop into many different types of cells such as the muscle cell, brain cell, skin cell, blood cell etc. For genomic research, the stem cell is invaluable.

Wormhole A wormhole is the reverse of a black hole. A black hole sucks in everything in its vicinity, whereas a wormhole spews out everything into outer space and that space could be a different universe from ours.

What is Life? This is a book – *What is Life? With Mind and Matter* – based on lectures in Dublin in 1943 by Erwin Schrödinger, one of the pioneers of quantum mechanics and Nobel Laureate in Physics in 1933. Cambridge University Press, 23rd print 2018, ISBN 978-1-107-60466-7.

ON GLOBAL ISSUES

Tagore's philosophical views and Quantum Mechanics

Figure 2.1   Rabindranath Tagore (Thakur) (1861 – 1941)

Rabindranath Tagore (actual Bengali name: Rabindranath Thakur) (1861–1941), the great Indian philosopher, was a Bengali poet and polymath. He lived during a transition period of Indian history in general and the Bengali culture in particular, when physics also went through revolutionary changes. Albert Einstein (1879-1955), the most prominent physicist of the 20th century, was the pioneer of modern physics who produced theories which advanced physics to unprecedented levels. Although Einstein produced the 'the principle of photoelectric effect' for which he received the Nobel Prize for physics and which was pivotal to the advent of quantum mechanics, he could not fully reconcile with the multifarious implications of quantum mechanics.

The two stalwarts of the first half of the 20th century met a number of times from 1926 onwards. When Tagore visited continental Europe and then America in 1930, they met at least four times in Berlin and New York. The meeting at Einstein's summer villa outside Berlin was of particular interest when they exchanged views and philosophical ideas extensively. During that meeting - poignantly described by Dmitri Marianoff, a journalist in the New York Times, as being between *Tagore, the poet with the head of a thinker, and Einstein, the thinker with the head of a poet'* - the two exchanged views on the reality of nature.

Einstein held the view that the world and, for that matter, the whole universe, is there independent of humanity. Tagore held the view that the world is a human world and hence without humanity, the world is irrelevant and non-existent. Einstein persisted and queried that aren't beauty and truth absolute and independent of man? Tagore disagreed and said that truth is realised through man and without man it does not exist. The whole conversation between these two giants was absolutely fascinating - it brought out the mindset of a scientist seeking out nature as it exists and that of a poet observing nature through the eyes and minds of human beings.

Einstein's commitment to the reality of nature was absolute, and that absolutism brought him into conflict with the quantum reality proposed by Niels Bohr, Werner Heisenberg and others. Einstein believed in the existence of causal, observer-independent reality; whereas quantum mechanics considers reality dependent on the act of observation. Bohr/Heisenberg proposed that an atomic particle such as an electron is there only when it is observed. If it is not observed, it is not there; it could be anywhere only to be described by quantum functional description. But Einstein would not accept that. He retorted by saying that the moon is there in the sky whether you observe it or not. Quantum mechanics states that an entity having unobserved presence cannot be claimed to be present with absolute certainty (with the probability of 1). Quantum mechanics tell us that the observer and the observed are entwined. The reality is not pre-ordained; reality is what is observed.

In 1928, Tagore received Arnold Sommerfeld, professor of theoretical physics at the University of Munich and a pioneer of atomic spectra, at Shantiniketan, West Bengal. Sommerfeld stated, *"Tagore is to India what Goethe* [pronounced as Görta] *is to Germany."* Sommerfeld's student Werner Heisenberg visited India the following year.

Heisenberg was one of the principal architects of quantum mechanics and his 'uncertainty principle' is the cornerstone of quantum mechanics. During the 1920s, he, along with Niels Bohr and others, produced what is now known as the 'Copenhagen Interpretation of quantum mechanics', where multiple existence of an atomic particle at different locations with superposition of quantum states was considered to be the reality of nature.

Although quantum mechanics had enormous success and explained various physical phenomena which classical physics was incapable of explaining, the conflict with Einstein on quantum mechanical fundamental assumptions of probabilistic description was deep rooted. Einstein considered quantum mechanics as an incomplete description of nature.

In 1929, when Heisenberg undertook a lecture tour around the world, he came to India. On 4 October 1929, he visited the University of Calcutta and in the afternoon, he visited Tagore. In fact, he was taken to Tagore's house at Jorasanko by the scientist Debendra Mohan Bose, a nephew of Jagadish Chandra Bose, and they had a number of conversations over the next few days. Heisenberg was very much impressed by Tagore's philosophical views. Fritjof Capra in his book *Uncommon Wisdom* wrote:

"In 1929 Heisenberg spent some time in India as the guest of the celebrated Indian poet Rabindranath Tagore, with whom he

had long conversations about science and Indian philosophy. The introduction to Indian thought brought Heisenberg great comfort. He began to see that the recognition of relativity, interconnectedness and impermanence as fundamental aspects of physical reality, which had been so difficult for himself and his fellow physicists, was the very basis of the Indian spiritual traditions."

Heisenberg said, *"After these conversations, some of the ideas that had seemed so crazy suddenly made much more sense. That was a great help for me."*

Heisenberg's comfort was to be seen in the context of a great intellectual battle that had been raging at that time between Einstein and Bohr/Heisenberg on the reality of nature. Indian mysticism or more accurately, Tagore's interpretation of Oriental (Brahma) philosophy, giving a support to modern physics and quantum theory, was undoubtedly a great comfort to Heisenberg. No wonder, Heisenberg even said after their conversations that Tagore reminded him of a prophet of the old days!

Tagore's philosophy of viewing the world with human eyes may seem to conflict with Einstein's observer-independent reality, but these are two perspectives of reality. Tagore's view of reality resonates very well with the quantum philosophy of observer-dependent reality.

Solzhenitsyn – from an ardent Communist to a devout Christian

Aleksandr Solzhenitsyn, 1 Dec 1918 – 3 Aug 2008, was a Russian novelist, short story writer, philosopher, historian and a political ideologist. Born a year after the Bolshevik revolution in Russia in October 1917 and in the immediate aftermath of World War I, his life and works were shaped by the harsh realities of life during his formative period and the consequences of war.

Figure 2.2   Aleksandr Solzhenitsyn

Solzhenitsyn's parents had all the trappings and background of Imperial Russia. His father, Isaakiy Solzhenitsyn, was an officer in the elite Cossack Brigade (which was fiercely Tsarist) of the Imperial Russian Army and his mother was the daughter of a wealthy landowner in the Kuban region in the northern foothills of the Caucasus. Thus, his family fitted the typical bourgeois family, as defined by the revolutionary Bolshevik party, against which the Bolshevik Revolution was carried out in 1917. His father died soon after his mother conceived him and so he was brought up by his widowed mother in extreme hardship, deprived of her wealth by the communist regime of Soviet Russia. Although he was to become a great literary giant, he studied Physics and Mathematics at Rostov State University.

As he grew up as an ardent communist, the drums of the next war (World War II) were beating louder and louder and, inevitably, he had to join the Russian Army against Nazi invasion to save his motherland. As a brilliant officer of Cossack heritage, he showed his military excellence and was twice decorated. But the war left a very painful imprint on him. He witnessed war crimes by the Soviet Army against German civilians – the non-combatants and the elderly were robbed of meagre possessions, women were gang raped and killed, houses were burnt and whole villages pillaged. On atrocities, he wrote in agony, "You know very well that we have come to take revenge against the Nazi atrocities in the Soviet Union."

While serving in the Red Army in WWII, he was arrested for derogatory remarks on the conduct of the war by Joseph Stalin in a private letter to a friend in 1945, just a couple of months before the end of the war and was sentenced to eight years' imprisonment in labour camps. He was in a prison in Moscow when on 9th May 1945 Germany surrendered. While the whole city erupted in jubilation, the person who fought for the country and risked his life was in the prison!

His sentence started in 1945. He chronicled his life in labour camps as forming three phases. In the last phase, from 1950 to

1953, he was in a 'Special Camp' for political prisoners in Kazakhstan, where he was forced to work as a miner, bricklayer and a foundry foreman. His experience during this time formed the basis of his novel *One day in the life of Ivan Denisovich* (1962). This was the only book that was allowed to be published in the Soviet Union after the reforms that were carried out by Nikita Khrushchev and, even then, only after Khrushchev's personal patronage. That reform also freed him from exile in 1956 and allowed him to go back to Moscow. His books, *Cancer Ward* (1968), *August 1914* (1971), *The Gulag Archipelago* (1973) and many more, were all published abroad.

Of all of his books, *The Gulag Archipelago* received most attention in the West, as it was in this book that he exposed the moral depravity of communist ideology. The Gulag, in Russian, is the acronym of the Main Directorate of Camps (labour). The book was written over a period of ten years taking materials from reports, interviews and diaries as well as legal documents and his own experiences. The three volumes of this book published in 1973 in the West led to his expulsion from the Soviet Union.

Solzhenitsyn was awarded the Nobel Prize in Literature in 1970 *"for the ethical force with which he has pursued the indispensable traditions of Russian literature"*. The authorities in the Soviet Union were very much angered by his supposedly anti-communist moral and ethical propaganda in the form of literary contributions. In 1974 the Soviet authorities withdrew his Soviet citizenship. He was flown to the then West Germany and after protracted negotiations, he was allowed to move his family to America in 1976. He lived in America from 1976 until 1994 when he returned to Russia after the fall of the Soviet Union. During this period, he wrote a dramatized account of the Russian Revolution of 1917 in *The Red Wheel*.

Although in the West he is portrayed as the voice against communism, a lone writer standing up to the might of an 'Evil Empire' etc., in reality, he was simply expressing his moral values – be it against communism or capitalism. He wrote a number of articles, while in America, showing the vacuousness of American capitalism and its moral degradation. He strongly criticised America for invading Iraq, Afghanistan and Kosovo. He wrote, *"In our country the lie has become not just a moral category but a pillar of the State."* This narrative is now relevant to many countries, East or West. He also wrote, *"Any man who has once proclaimed violence as his method is inevitably forced to take the lie as his principle."* It may have been written against the backdrop of Joseph Stalin's atrocities and violent measures in WWII, but it also applies very well to modern day politicians – democratically elected leaders in Western affluent countries.

In 1994, Solzhenitsyn returned to Russia with his wife and lived in the western part of Moscow. Although he lived over 17 years in America, he never accepted the American culture and way of life. As he became old, he moved away from socialism and became a devout Russian Orthodox Christian. He died on 3 August 2008 of a heart attack.

After Solzhenitsyn's death, the literary circles in the West and in Russian started carrying out dispassionate assessments of his political, moral and religious views. Although he was a devoted Christian all his life, after his return to Russia in 1994 he became a fervent Christian. But his devout Christianity did not lead him to denigrate other religions or to become an anti-Semite, as some critics had alleged. The Jewish novelist Elie Wiesel disagreed with such aspersions against his character and wrote that Solzhenitsyn was "too intelligent, too honest, too courageous and too great a writer" to be an anti-Semite.

International Mother Language Day

Language is the most important and principal method of communication between humans and only language sets us apart from other animals. Yes, animals do communicate by making noises, by sign language or by body language. But we, the Homo sapiens, have taken the method of communication to a higher level by inventing language comprising letters, words, punctuation etc., in structured forms to convey our feelings by oral and written methods.

Thus, language confers on us our mode of expression, our identity, our existential experience. We inherit it from our mothers, almost through the umbilical cord - like blood, like nutrition. We develop our tongue like our mothers' and that is why it is called the mother tongue and the language is called the mother language.

So, when language is challenged, the very identity is challenged. That is what happened immediately after the creation of Pakistan in 1947. The *Two Nation Theory (TNT)* propounded by Allama Iqbal in 1930 and supported by Mohammad Ali Jinnah to establish a separate Muslim State called Pakistan in India was the beginning of political Islam in India. The low-level sectarianism that had existed in India for centuries had then been uplifted to communalism and patriotism with the support of the opportunistic Muslim and Hindu politicians.

The Indian subcontinent was divided into India and Muslim Pakistan in August 1947. The province of East Pakistan comprising 55% of the whole country's population was entirely Bengali speaking, whereas West Pakistan having 45% of the population had Punjabi, Sindhi, Baluchi as well as Urdu speaking people; with Urdu spoken by about 7% of the population.

The fault line between the two provinces appeared less than a year after the partition when Mohammad Ali Jinnah declared in a speech on 21st March 1948 at the racecourse in Dhaka that Urdu would be the only state language of this country. It was an injustice of a monumental scale. It was an attempt to rob the mother language of 55% of the people and impose Urdu in the name of Islam.

Students from university level downwards felt betrayed and humiliated. Only a few months before, they spearheaded the creation of the Muslim State on the assumption that the two provinces would be self-governing with their own culture and their own language. Even Sheikh Mujibur Rahman, as a student leader, went to Guwahati, Assam, in 1946 with more than 500 students from Calcutta to campaign in the plebiscite in Assam for Pakistan. Now they were at the brink of losing their language, their identity!

The students' movement started to grow; low level local protests merged into sub-district and district levels. From 1948 to 1952 students' grievances and anger were palpable and at boiling point. They felt that they had been made to jump at the behest of the politicians, religious leaders and above all their parents, from the frying pan into the fire!

The students took a decision to observe the Language Movement Day on 21 February 1952 throughout the whole province and Dhaka University students took the lead. The government declared Section 144 of the Penal Code in Dhaka and banned all assemblies of more than five people. But schools, colleges and universities were left open and so assemblies of five or more people were inevitable. The government of Pakistan wanted to teach a brutal lesson to the arrogant and disobedient students and thereby to the people of the province!

*Figure 2.3   Students gathering at the Dhaka University Arts Faculty
Campus in 1952*

The students started gathering at the Dhaka University Arts
Faculty campus in the morning of 21st February. They wanted to
express their demand that Bengali should be one of the national
languages of the country. Slowly and cautiously, they emerged
through the main gate of the campus and turned left towards the
Dhaka Medical College. They had no weapons of any sort and

had only placards. Hardly had the front of the demonstration moved 100 metres or so, when the waiting police at the edge of the campus opened fire on the students. Five students died almost instantly with blood spilling over the street and more than 17 students were seriously injured. In less than five years since the creation of Pakistan, the students had to pay with their own blood for the sins of their fathers (and their sins too) for opting for a Muslim State!

Figure 2.4 The first Shaheed Minar (Martyr's Monument) built on 23rd Feb 1952

A day later, the university students along with medical college students started building a monument in memory of their fallen students at the side of the road, which was only a stone's throw away from the campus, and it was completed on 23rd

February. The police came and with all their brutality desecrated the memorial and demolished the monument. It was an insult to the memory of the martyred students and an all-out onslaught on the people of East Pakistan. However, a few days later, on 26th February 1952, the editor of the local Bengali newspaper, the *Daily Azad*, inaugurated a new monument within the compound of the Medical College and it was named as the Shaheed Minar – the Martyrs' Monument.

The government of Pakistan eventually accepted Bengali as one of the national languages of Pakistan, when the National Assembly adopted it on 7th May 1954. In Pakistan's first Constitution in 1956, Bengali and Urdu were given the status of national languages under Article 214.

But what led to the bloodshed of students on the streets of Dhaka could not be swept away any more. The constant denigration of Bengali culture and language by the Pakistani government, economic subjugation, employment disparity etc., added fuel to the fire of the language movement. On 26th March 1971, the Pakistani military junta launched an unprovoked attack with full military force on civilians and on the Dhaka University students and teachers to teach another lesson. The hitherto tenuous link of Muslim fraternity between the East and West had then broken down completely and after nine months of brutal war, Pakistan had to surrender, and Bangladesh achieved liberation on the 16th of December 1971.

Thus, Bangladesh became the first and only country in the world that fought for and gained the freedom to preserve the mother language. In recognition of the unique sacrifice that the Bangladeshis made to establish Bengali as the national language, *UNESCO* accorded 21st February as the International Mother Language Day. This day is celebrated throughout the whole world, wherever Bengalis are. The Bengali language is the fifth largest language in the world and is spoken by nearly 275 million people – Bangladesh (162 million), West Bengal (100 million) in India, and the diaspora of Bengalis in the world (13 million). The

97

top five languages are: 1. Mandarin Chinese (1051 million); 2. English (510 million); 3. Hindi (490 million); 4. Spanish (420 million) and 5. Bengali 275 million. Bengali is also one of the culturally richest languages in the world, enriched by Rabindranath Tagore (Nobel Laureate in Literature in 1912), Nazrul Islam, DL Roy, Atul Prasad, Bankim Chandra and many more.

Tagore and Bengali identity

*If there is one person who embodies Bengal, Bengali language
and culture that must be Tagore.*

Bangladesh was liberated from the yoke of Pakistani domination
in 1971 as the land of Bangla (বাংলা) speaking people, not as an
outpost of the alien culture of Pakistan or the Middle East. What
started as the language movement, following the brutal killing in
1952 of university students demanding Bengali as a national
language, eventually turned into 'linguistic nationalism' that
culminated in the liberation of Bangladesh.

For 24 long years, from 1947 to 1971, Pakistan tried to impose
Urdu as the national language of Pakistan and to obliterate
Bengali language and Bengali culture from the indigenous
population of the then East Pakistan. The leaders of Pakistan
implanted and patronised Islamism in East Pakistan and that
helped to evolve Razakar, al-Badr and many other factions of
Islamist organisations during the liberation war not only to
defeat the nationalist movement but also to wipe out Bengaliness
among the people. But they failed. These Razakars changed their
guise but maintained their 'Muslimness' as an opposition force
against the dominant cultural identity of the people in post-
independent Bangladesh.

The people with 'Muslim' identity might have retreated
temporarily following the defeat of their patron, Pakistan, but
they were not beaten. They kept reappearing, as and when an
opportunity arose, to undermine Bengali language and culture.
The other arm of their strategy is to propagate Islamic culture as
a replacement of Bengali culture. The proliferation of the 'hijab',
'niqab' and 'burqa' among Bangladeshi women, the trend of
inserting adjuncts like 'bin' or 'bint' (for men and women
respectively) in names, the increasing use of Arabic words

replacing common Bengali words, all testify cultural invasion under the guise of religion.

This twin strategy of undermining Bengali language and culture, and the import of alien culture had become apparent during the period of military rule in Bangladesh from 1975 to 1992 and then whenever the Islamic-oriented political party, the Bangladesh Nationalist Party (BNP), often supported by the more overtly Islamist organisations like Jamaat-e-Islam, came to power. Of late, in anticipation of the BNP coming to power in the national election in 2008, these 'Muslim' identity people at the behest of the BNP were gearing up and attacking Bengali language and culture.

Although Willem van Schendel, in his book *A History of Bangladesh,* identified two competing identity groups distinguishing them as (i) 'Bengaliness' that upholds Bangladesh as the homeland for Bengalis and embraces the linguistic community of Tagore, Nazrul, Bankim, Madhushudan, Jasimuddin, Jibanananda Das, Sarat Chandra, Golam Mostafa and so forth and (ii) 'Bangladeshiness' which takes the view that Bangladesh is, in effect, a logical outcome of Pakistan and the homeland of Muslim Bengal. As the argument goes, without Pakistan, Bangladesh would not have come into existence and hence Bangladesh remains Muslim, and it is 'overwhelmingly and essentially Muslim'. (They conveniently forget or ignore the fact that during the liberation struggle they did everything to stop Bangladesh coming into existence and now they are claiming it to be Muslim Bangladesh!)

This second group, despite Schendel's branding it as 'Bangladeshiness', is a misnomer and gross misrepresentation. It should rightly be put under 'Muslimness', as they put Muslim as their prime identity and their country affiliation comes far below. They accept disgruntledly Bengali as the national language, but many of them would happily accept Urdu as the national language, which conforms to their Muslim identity. They are, in effect, the remnants of the Pakistani period.

100

Bengali is one of the richest languages in the world. It is the direct descendant of Sanskrit, which is a Proto-Indo-European language that has evolved over four millennia. That is why one can find similarities and resemblances between many Bengali words and Italian, English and Cyrillic words.

Figure 2.5   Rabindranath Tagore

Of all the Bengali litterateurs, the person who stands out head and shoulders above the rest is Rabindranath Tagore, who was the poet, essayist, novelist, song writer and composer, playwright, philosopher and educationalist. He was simply a literary giant not only in India but also in the whole world. He was the only person from the Indian subcontinent who was awarded a Nobel Prize for Literature (1913) and his songs are sung as national anthems in two sovereign states – India and Bangladesh.

If there is one person who embodies Bengal and Bengali language and culture that must be Tagore. Although he was born in Kolkata, his ancestors were from Jessore in Bangladesh. Tagore married Mrinalini Devi who hailed from Khulna in the then East Bengal. Tagore spent more than two decades looking after the zamindari in East Bengal and spent extended periods in Shilaidaha, Kushtia; Shahjadpur, Pabna; and Patishar, Rajshahi; all in East Bengal. His poetic genius, his philosophy and his perception of life were all moulded by the everyday lives of people in this part of East Bengal. He wrote many famous poems, songs and short stories while he was in the houseboat (called Padma) in Shilaidaha and Shahjadpur. The most famous book of poems 'Sonar Tari' (সোনার তরী) (The Golden Boat) was written in those days. He gave poetic expressions to occasions such as Bengali New Year (বাংলা নববর্ষ), welcoming the rainy season (বর্ষাবরণ), the spring festival (বসন্ত উৎসব) and so on that ripple through the hearts and minds of Bengali people the world over.

Tagore felt very strongly for the plight of his poor Muslim tenants (প্রজা). One such occasion was narrated by Krisna Dutta like this: When he called a meeting of his tenants one afternoon, he noticed that the Hindu tenants were sitting on mattresses and the poor Muslim tenants were sitting on grass farther apart. He was cross at this segregation and asked his tenants that everyone must sit together on mattresses; if there was not enough space on mattresses, everyone must sit on the grass. Quite often he would relieve his poor Muslim tenants of taxes and that did not endear him to his father, Debendranath Tagore.

There is a concerted move by the 'Muslim' identity people – the Islamists and Islamist sympathisers - to denigrate Tagore by egregious falsification and trumped-up stories. They branded Tagore as a plagiarist, a second-rate poet who attained fame only by British patronage. Needless to say, any attempt to counter such grossly egregious allegations is like going into the dirty gutters with them.

Also, it had been said by those blockheaded morons that Tagore was anti-Muslim as, they assert, he wrote a number of poems praising Hindu culture and Hindu religion; he wrote none for Islam. That is quite frankly utterly ridiculous. As a Hindu (in fact he was a follower of the Brahmo-Samaj), it was quite natural that he would write about these religions; that does not imply that he was against Islam or Jain or Buddhism. Did he write anything against Islam? No. No. No. So, how on earth, could he be called an anti-Muslim or racist?

Only one point that merits addressing here is that he had been accused of opposing the establishment of Dhaka University. It was possible that he was not enthusiastic about Dhaka University as he was in the process of setting up his own University at that time, which came into existence in the same year that Dhaka University did. But, later on, he supported Dhaka University when adequate financial provisions were made. He could not have opposed it strongly, as brazen Islamists claim, on grounds of race or religion, because in East Bengal in those days an overwhelmingly large fraction (between 70 to 75%) of educated people primed to go to the university were Hindus. So, Tagore's opposition to Dhaka University would have affected predominantly Hindus. The problem with semi-literate Islamists is that they think that he opposed Dhaka University because it was in Muslim-Bangladesh! How ridiculous!

Syed Abul Maksud, in his book *Purabange Rabindranath* (পূর্ববঙ্গে রবীন্দ্রনাথ) (Rabindranath in East Bengal), stated that Tagore had cordial relations with Muslims in East Bengal. The Muslim aristocrat of Dhaka, Nawab Sir Salimullah *"paid rich tributes to the greatest poetical genius of modern India"* in a meeting organized in the city on 26 November 1913 to celebrate his Nobel Prize award. Maksud also pointed out that Tagore was given a very enthusiastic reception by the Salimullah Muslim Hall Students' Union of the University of Dhaka on the 10th of February 1926 during his second and last visit to Dhaka. It may be pointed out that Dhaka University was founded only five years previously. (If Tagore had opposed it, then SM Hall Students' Union was probably ignorant about it and now nearly 100 years later the brazen Islamists had discovered it!) It should also be pointed out that the University of Dhaka awarded Tagore an honorary doctorate in 1936.

To say that Tagore had opposed Dhaka University is totally disingenuous and dishonest. Also, the accusation that he was against Muslims has a racist connotation. The 'Muslim' identity people are hell-bent on carrying out a character assassination of Tagore and thereby undermine the very essence of the 'Bengali' identity of the Bangladeshi people. The sooner these clandestine agents doing Pakistan's bidding for 'Muslimness' are exposed, the better it is for the country.

Egregious allegations of communalism against Rabindranath

Rabindranath Tagore (1861-1941) lived through a very turbulent phase in Indian and world history – the period when the British Raj attained the peak of its colonial power and exercised the most brutal authoritarian rule in India, the period when Bengal (the state which allowed the first foothold of British merchants in India at the beginning of the 18th century) was partitioned off and then annulled, the period of two world wars and the period which saw the rise of the unstoppable swadeshi (self-rule) movement.

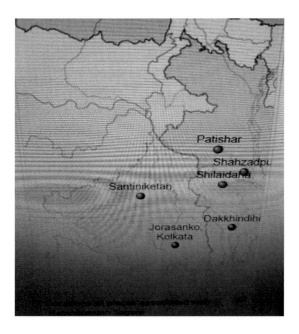

Figure 2.6   Places which Rabindranath Tagore was associated with

A poet, a novelist, a litterateur, an artist, a reformer, in short, a myriad of a man, Rabindranath Tagore lived and died in the thick of actions. He not only advanced Bengali language and culture to the world scene but also gave Bengalis - Hindus and Muslims alike - their self-esteem, identity and cultural heritage. His songs are used as national anthems in India as well as in Bangladesh and Sri Lanka's national anthem drew inspirations from his song.

However, a large section of Bangladeshi die-hard Muslims with the mind-set of Pakistani tribalism and religious antagonism towards Hindus had been sniping at Tagore ever since the creation of Bangladesh in 1971. The allegations ranged from Rabindranath being communal and anti-Muslim, citing that he opposed the partition of Bengal to deny the Muslims a separate homeland and that he opposed setting up of Dhaka University etc. All of these allegations were utterly egregious and the conjecture of bigoted minds.

Many Bengali Muslims who lay such allegations on Rabindranath quote Major General (Retd) M A Matin's book *Amader Swadhinata Sangramer Dharabahikata ebong Prasangik kicchu Katha* (Chronology of our freedom struggle and some associated discussions) published by Ahmad Publishing House, Dhaka in 2000. The retired Army Officer placed most of his allegations on heresy without any substantiation or corroboration and packaged such opinions as statement of facts!

The author, M A Matin, implied throughout the book that Rabindranath was an orthodox Hindu and hence anti-Muslim and that was why he opposed the partition of Bengal. As further evidence of his anti-Muslim character, he was stated to have opposed the setting up of Dacca (now Dhaka) University.

Let us look at the stated allegations that Rabindranath was an orthodox Hindu and anti-Muslim and the reason behind his opposition to the partition of Bengal. And then I would look into his attitude towards Dhaka University.

If one looks into Tagore's ancestry over the last few centuries, one will find that Tagore's Brahmin clan, who hailed from Jessore, had a long and close association with Muslims. Two Tagore Brahmin brothers in Jessore were close to a man named Mohammad Tahir Pir Ali, the wazir of the governor of Jessore, who himself was a Brahmin but converted to Islam for matrimonial and financial reasons. Tahir Pir Ali tricked the Tagore brothers to smell and eventually eat meat (probably beef) and because of that event the brothers were expelled from the orthodox Brahmin sect. However, their whole family remained Brahmins and the brothers were ostracised as 'Pirali Brahmins'. (*Ref: Rabindranath Tagore, The myriad-minded man by Krishna Dutta & Andrew Robinson, Bloomsbury Publishing, UK*).

These two brothers (Pirali Brahmins) eventually left Jessore due possibly to social antagonism and moved to Calcutta (now Kolkata). The descendents of one of these two brothers were two brothers called Darpanarayan, who settled at Pathuriaghat (whose descendant includes Sharmila Tagore) and Nilmoni (the great-great-grandfather of Rabindranath) who settled at Jorasanko. His descendant, Rabindranath's grandfather, Dwarkanath, a flamboyant zamindar, and his son Debendranath, Rabindranath's father, started the Brahmo Samaj, which was a sort of philosophical belief more akin to Buddhism and animism. Now, to allege that Rabindranath Tagore, a Pirali Brahmin, was an orthodox Brahmin and an anti-Muslim would be very much mendacious and deceitful. Rabindranath published a book called *The Religion of Man* which advanced a belief embodying humanity, a belief of human consciousness merging into the limitless creation of universe – *shimar majhe ashim tumi.* Rabindranath Tagore's description of his family as depicted in *The Religion of Man* was, *"The unconventional code of life for our family has been a confluence of three cultures, the Hindu, Mohammedan and British."*

In his writings, Rabindranath always showed empathy with the Muslims. In his novel called *Ghare Baire* (The Home and the

World), the main character, a Hindu zamindar, stated quite boldly that he would not condone Swadeshi activities if that meant hurting his Muslim subjects – those people were utterly poor people, they did not have the luxury of boycotting foreign goods and lose their living. In the story, the zamindar gave up his life when he went to protect his Muslim subjects in the ensuing Hindu-Muslim riot. Rabindranath was roundly criticised for such narratives.

It is beyond dispute that Rabindranath opposed the partition of Bengal, not because he wanted to deny the Muslims a separate homeland but because he wanted Hindus and Muslims to live together in amity and harmony, as they had been doing for centuries. Moreover, it was pure common sense and quite natural for the Tagore clan to oppose the partition, because Tagore's roots were in East Bengal - Tagore's zamindari was in Shilaidaha (Kushtia, now in Bangladesh), Rabindranath's wife, Mrinalini was from Jessore (now the district of Khulna, Bangladesh) (Jessore and Khulna were one district called Jessore until 1892); Ref. *Islam o Rabindranath Anyanya Prasanga* (Islam and Rabindranath's other matters), *by Amitabh Chowdhury, ISBN No. 81-7293-188-3.* The Tagore family always maintained close ties with their ancestral home ever since they moved to Kolkata. The partition would deprive the Tagore family of its roots. The partition of Bengal was implemented on October 16, 1905. On the day of partition, Rabindranath peacefully and in a friendly gesture initiated the Rakhibandhan (the tying of Rakhi, meaning friendship). The partition was, however, annulled on December 12, 1911.

The very stipulation that the proposed partition of East Bengal would provide a homeland for the Muslims was ludicrous and block-headed in those days. Those brain-washed Muslims who propagate this view of a separate homeland for Muslims are trying to backfit 1940s events (demand for Pakistan) back into the 1900s to tarnish Rabindranath's character for opposing the partition of Bengal.

It was stated in MA Matin's above-mentioned book that on March 28th 1912, a huge meeting was organised at *Garer Math*, Kolkata, to protest against the proposed setting up of Dhaka University and that meeting was presided over by Rabindranath Tagore. Afterwards, a delegation of top-level Hindu leaders went to meet Lord Hardinge, the then Viceroy of India, and warned him that the establishment of Dhaka University would face a similar fate to the partition of Bengal. However, there was no reference to or corroboration of Rabindranath's attendance in the *Garer Math* meeting in MA Matin's book, simply his unsubstantiated assertion. AZM Abdul Ali, editorial board member of the literary magazine *Kali o Kolom*, in an article immediately after the publication of MA Matin's book, disputed the statement that Rabindranath attended the meeting and asked MA Matin to provide a reference or source of his information, but there was no reply from Matin or anybody else!

An article by Asahabur Rahman in the *Dhaka Tribune* on May 16, 2018, stated that a search in the Tagore archives showed that on March 28th 1912, Rabindranath was at Shilaidaha. He left Kolkata on March 24th and stayed at Shilaidaha until April 12th recuperating from his illness. He composed 17 poems and songs during those days and, as he usually put the date and name of the place where he composed a piece, he put Shilaidaha as the place where those pieces were composed during that period. So, how could Rabindranath possibly be in Kolkata on March 28th, as MA Matin asserted? Such baseless accusations are typical of bigoted minds.

Dhaka University was established on the basis of recommendations made by the Nathan Commission, appointed by the government of Bengal, on May 27th, 1912. However, due to the outbreak of World War I (August 1914 – November 1918), the Commission's recommendations were shelved and then nearer the end of the war, the government of India established another Commission - the Saddler Commission - in November 1917 to look into that outstanding matter. On the basis of positive recommendation by the Saddler Commission in March 1919, Dhaka University was eventually established in 1921.

Rabindranath visited Dhaka in February 1926 as a guest of Nawab of Dhaka, Khwaja Habibullah. He was given three receptions by Dhaka University – two were organised by the Dhaka University Central Students Union (DUCSU) held at the Curzon Hall and the other at Salimullah Muslim Hall (S M Hall) organised by the students of the Hall. If Tagore had been against the establishment of Dhaka University, it was highly unlikely that within five years the students at the university would forget all about his opposition and extend a warm welcome and give cordial receptions by the Muslim and Hindu students alike! In addition, various institutions and organisations in Dhaka such as the Jagannath College, Dhaka Collegiate School, Hindu-Muslim Seba Sangha, Dhaka Municipality and the Peoples' Association etc., organised special receptions for him.

So, where is the evidence of Tagore's opposition to the establishment of Dhaka University? MA Matin made the allegations against Tagore without any foundation, without any evidence. Professor Rafiqul Islam of Dhaka University wrote a book entitled *Dhaka Bisshobidyaloyer Ashi Bochor* (Dhaka University's eighty years) based on his long research. His findings didn't support MA Matin's assertions at all. Some of the Bengali Muslim writers, now and in the recent past, blinded by Islamic zeal, tied up Tagore's opposition to the Bengal partition (which he opposed in order to maintain communal harmony) and fabricated Tagore's opposition to Dhaka University to make up a well-rounded story of Tagore's anti-Muslimness! It is a classic case of joining up a lie with a truth and packaging the whole thing as truth.

The Origins of the Bengali Calendar

Figure 2.7   Pahela Baishakh celebration in Dhaka, Bangladesh

Every year on the 14th of April, Bangladesh traditionally celebrates Bengali New Year's Day (Bangla *Noboborsho*) with great razzmatazz – they don colourful festoons on apartments of high-rise buildings, on transport vehicles including rickshaws and even on lamp posts; women wear bright yellow saris chanting *Noboborsho* - welcoming songs; girls with garlands in their hands walk the streets, as if to offer garlands to the exalted soul of the New Year.

An unprecedented air of jubilation and a feeling of festivity overtake the minds of the people. It is a cultural occasion that overrides the strict religious constraints that men, women and children have to endure throughout the whole year. It is an occasion when people open up and join together in an air of conviviality. Celebrations continue throughout the whole day and well into the evening and such celebrations are not limited to only cosmopolitan cities; people in smaller towns and even villages embrace the occasion too.

But a few years back, an ugly incident marred that occasion very badly. The city dwellers of the capital city, Dhaka, were enjoying their time. As darkness fell – though there were bright lights all around – vicious sexual predators in gangs of twenty or so rounded up the singing and celebrating women in public places in and around the Dhaka University campus. These vicious gangs surrounded women and started molesting them in full public view.

There were, of course, sort-of pussycat police officers around too scared to intervene and rescue the women. These police officers on duty gave the impression that they were there to celebrate the party, not to maintain law and order which would require intervening in such public disturbances!

Even the Bangladeshi general public, who were normally viewed as always helpful to the weak and distressed, looked on as simple bystanders, when the goons kept on assaulting the hapless women. Only a few brave souls rescued some women under attack, and in the process suffered physical injury. Traumatised women dashed into nearby buildings to escape from these human hyenas. Police offered little or no help at all.

Soul-searching and deep introspection by conscientious people commenced, querying how and why such thuggery took place in a peaceful atmosphere in public, and who these thugs were.

What transpired within the next two weeks was that the sexual predator religious goons, perhaps Jamaat-e-Islam people, and people with fundamentalist ideas as well as outright sex maniacs, viewed such *Noboborsho* celebrations as nothing but an incursion to, and erosion of Islamic culture in the country by the Hindu culture. Their view was that the Bengali New Year is non-Islamic and should had no place in Muslim Bangladesh.

Such a view that Bangla *Noboborsho* and the Bangla calendar were intrusions from the Hindu culture to Muslim Bangladesh was not only blatantly communal and racist, but also grossly misconceived. This madrassa-educated, totally moronic cadre of mullahs emerged and alleged something without any basic understanding. Their assertion could not be further from the truth.

Let us delve deep into the background of the Bengali Calendar and show how the 14th of April 2015 was taken to usher in 1422 BS (Bangla Sôn).

The third Mughal Emperor, Muhammad Akbar (also known as Akbar the Great), was instrumental in promulgating a new Bengali Calendar after modifying the then existing calendar. He did so in order to facilitate administrative procedures and to fix a firm tax collection date in Bengal. At that time, the calendar that was used was known as Tarikh-e-Elahi, which followed the Islamic lunar calendar. The lunar year consisted of twelve months but had 354 or 355 days (following 12 lunar orbits round the earth). Thus, there was a drift of about 10 or 11 days every year between the lunar and solar (Gregorian) calendars.

That created a major practical problem. A firm date (for that matter any date) fixed for the collection of taxes, normally designated at the end of the harvest period, gradually came forward by about 11 days every year and fell out of season. That meant that whereas a tax collection date might have been originally fixed after the harvest period, it gradually drifted forward and became a date prior to the harvest after a few years. This created immense misery to the farmers to pay taxes before the harvest!

Realising that practical problem, Mughal Emperor Akbar along with the royal astronomer, Amir Fathullah Shirazi developed the Bengali calendar. It was a synthesis of the Islamic lunar calendar and the modern solar calendar of 365 days (366 leap year days).

The year when Akbar took over the reign of the Mughal Empire was 1556 *CE* (Common Era) (previously called AD). That year in the Islamic calendar was 963 AH (Anno Hegirae). He promulgated that a new calendar year would be started on the 1st of Muharram (which was the first month in the Islamic calendar) in that year of 963 AH.

Following that system, the year would follow the solar year (365 days) and so no mismatch between the new calendar and the seasons would arise from that time. That calendar was used over the centuries as the Bangla Calendar with Bangla names for the months (Boishakh, Jyoishto, Ashar etc.). However, that calendar was slightly revised during the Pakistan days by a committee headed by Dr Mohammad Shahidullah under the auspices of the Bangla Academy in 1966. That revised version (when 14th April was fixed as the beginning of the year) was adopted officially in Bangladesh in 1987. That is the calendar that ushers in the Bengali New Year.

Now the question is how did we get to the year of 1422 BS on the 14th of April 2015 CE? The following consideration would show how it is done. As the start of this calendar was 1556 CE (Akbar's accession to the throne), which was also the beginning of the Islamic year 963 AH, 459 years (2015 CE – 1556 CE) had passed since then until now. Now adding 459 years to the Islamic year of 963 AH (when the system started), we get 1422. This is how we have the New Year of 1422 BS that year.

Also, one can analyse the difference between the Bengali calendar and the Islamic calendar. The Islamic year in 2015 CE was 1436 AH, whereas the Bengali year is 1422 BS. The time when the divergence took place was 1556 CE and during these intervening 459 years (2015-1556) the Islamic calendar fell short by 459 x 11 = 5049 days with regard to solar calendar. This then produced just over 14 years (5049/355) in the Islamic calendar. In other words, an extra 14 years were produced in the Islamic calendar since the commencement of the Bengali calendar, and that explains why it was 1436 AH, but 1422 BS.

The adoption and modification of calendars are done by many countries – Islamic or non-Islamic – to suit their needs. Iran uses the Solar Hijri calendar, called the Sham Hijri (SH), which begins with the vernal equinox (the start of spring in the northern hemisphere). The length of time between the vernal equinox and the autumnal equinox is about 186 days and 10 hours and the other cycle is 178 days. Afghanistan uses a slight variation of the Iranian calendar. West Bengal uses a Bengali calendar where the New Year's Day is 15th April.

Figure 2.8   Bangladesh Chhatra Union formed a human chain near Dhaka University's Raju Sculpture the following Monday demanding immediate arrest and punishment for those who sexually assaulted several women during the Bengali New Year celebrations.

Thus, we can categorically dismiss any claim that the Bengali calendar belongs to a Hindu religion or culture and that following this calendar is un-Islamic. Such assertions are utter nonsense and racist.

The attack on women when they were celebrating the Bengali New Year (Noboborsho) was totally barbaric and pure thuggery.

Those religious bigots who came out with naked religious claims in support of such thuggery should hang their heads in shame, because there was no religious basis whatsoever nor moral justification for such behaviour.

Frankenstein on the March

Figure 2.9   Interconnections making up the world wide web

Victor Frankenstein's creation of a human monster, known simply as Frankenstein, in the 19th century novel *Frankenstein or The Modern Prometheus* by Mary Wollstonecraft Shelley may be a pure fantasy, but there is an uncanny similarity to that in the modern-day world. However, that fictional monster was made to disappear in the icy wilderness of the north; but the modern-day monster is firmly embedded in present-day technology and is going nowhere. This newly produced monster is so powerful and ubiquitous that it threatens to take over the human mind, relegate human beings to the backburner and control their lives. If God is viewed as an all-powerful, all-knowledgeable, all-embracing entity, then this is it; it is the de facto God.

What is this all-powerful, all-knowledgeable entity that overrules human beings? It is, in fact, a human invention of ethereal dimensions. It exists in ethernet – something like fictitious ether which pervades the whole world, the whole universe, but nobody has actually seen it or identified it; it exists in cyberspace, somewhere up in the cloud, in the sky. Doesn't it sound like a god of some sort? But there is a sharp distinction. It does not go into heaven and hell dimensions. It is quite happy controlling human minds, treating human beings as subjugated animals.

It is the World Wide Web, abbreviated as www, where information – documents, images, audio and video clips and links, etc. – can be accessed in cyberspace by millions and billions of users worldwide almost instantly. With the astounding progress in computer technology, where miniaturisation and the speed of data processing have gone up exponentially higher year after year over the last decade or so, computers have become indispensable tools for human beings. And this computer technology has spawned desktops, laptops, palmtops, smart phones, iPhones, Kindle Fire and all other gadgets of indescribable variety. All these gadgets are woven together in the internet so that people can do all sorts of hitherto unimaginable things.

Gone are the days when pen and paper were essential tools for human intellectual endeavour. Whereas previously people needed to be literate to require pen and paper, now people can use this internet facility without much of a literary background. One can express one's opinion, such as liking an idea by just clicking into the 'like' button. One can express one's emotion by attaching various facial expressions called emojis. One can express one's strongly held conviction in 140 characters in Twitter. One can upload images from mobile/cell phones straight into emails and share them with friends, relations or a wider public right across the world. The opportunities (and pitfalls) are simply boundless.

When all of these processes and activities are put together, they can be described in modern-day terminology as 'social media'. Social media are the computer-based social networks for communicating, sharing and exchanging information between members of virtual communities round the world. There has been an unprecedented proliferation of various types of social media — Facebook, Skype, Google, LinkedIn, Twitter, Instagram, YouTube, Flickr, Pinterest, Messenger, Messages, WhatsApp and many more — each vying for the custom of the general public and offered completely free of charge. The more people use their platforms, criss-crossing messages across the world, the happier and richer they become. It is like an open house — come and feast yourself to your heart's content, given all free of charge!

So, how do these deceptively most generous and charitable organisations employing thousands of people, if not tens of thousands, across the globe survive without charging users a single penny or a dime? That is the trick of the trade. That is where the Frankenstein simile comes in.

The Facebook founder, Mark Zuckerberg, who established the free network in the 1990s, had the stated purpose of connecting people with each other - to empower them, to give them voice, to make them count. Other platform owners also expressed similar sentiments such that people might mistakenly think that they are modern-day angels. But there is no such thing as a free lunch.

These supposedly 'charitable' social media organisations are 'data' traders. They make you, me and everybody else come and exchange views using their facilities. People are free to talk about anything and everything on earth, as long as it is not racially loaded, terrorist-related, brazenly threatening to others, etc. This restrictive clause effectively makes users liable for the propriety of information that is exchanged, not the platform owners. But the platform owner effectively owns the proprietary rights of data, although all of it has been in the public domain. The underlying reason is that the data have been recorded and stored in the owner's machines and so the owner can do whatever he likes, as long as it does not violate the Data Protection Act 2018 in the UK or the General Data Protection Regulation (GDPR) 2016/679 in the European Union.

When someone clicks 'like' on a certain item, when someone puts a small cryptic comment, when someone uploads an image, all these stray items can be put together and a comprehensive picture or profile of that person can be built up. As a recent example, a reporter investigating Donald Trump's use of psychographics in the presidential election campaign in 2016, went to see Cambridge Analytica in London, which devised the methodology of psychographics for the population and applied it to the American population. The head of Cambridge Analytica (CA) told him that by using totally innocuous data, which are all in the public domain, they can create a very good personal profile of a group of people or an individual through using their highly sophisticated algorithm.

To show the validity of the CA algorithm, he said that he had produced a personal profile of the reporter – all from data in the public domain. He told him that the journalist was a history graduate from a certain university (he even told him his grade), his family background, his political affiliation, his religious background, his atheistic leaning, his foreign tours, his eating habits, his liking of French wines, Italian shoes, etc. The reporter was literally shocked to bits to see that his life was such an open book. CA knows almost everything about him – his mind, his thinking and liking, his affiliations, etc. And worst of all, he was totally unaware that he had himself given out so much information about himself!

Cambridge Analytica had just collected all stray data and processed them. It is all done by electronic means on an industrial scale. Individual profiles can lead to psychographics and people with similar psychographics can be banded together for political, economic and social purposes. Once CA had completed the psychographics, the information available to the Trump camp was passed on to publicity and campaign groups and they literally targeted individuals with appropriate pitch, knowing very well their minds, their liking and disliking, their mode of thinking, etc.

These 'data traders' are literally sitting on gold mines. Each one of these supposedly 'charitable' social media organisations is worth billions, if not tens or hundreds of billions of dollars. Money literally comes falling down on them from the sky or spurts out of the ground.

They are the modern-day gods – they know the hearts and minds of people, more than people know of themselves. With the knowledge of people's minds, they can control their behaviour, aspirations, lifestyles, etc, and that is where the power of these gods lies.

Human beings have created www and the www has spawned data collection opportunities through various platforms. Cambridge Analytica is just putting souls into the bodies and thereby becoming gods. Now these gods/Frankensteins know more about us than we know about ourselves. They can manipulate our minds, our thinking, our aspirations in such a way that we never thought was possible. We have become their subordinate entities. The Frankensteins have made Britain leave the EU and have produced the most unthinkable and unsuitable American president. Who knows what Frankenstein will do next? Frankenstein is on the march. (Note: The CA and its parent company, SCL, filed for insolvency on 1 May 2018 and closed operations).

Frailty in our ubiquitous democracy

In the 1950s and 1960s, communism and socialism and their various shades swept across the whole world, particularly across the developing world. Those politico-economic dogmas, however, did not or could not take a firm grip on most of those countries. They came about as the utopian sentimentality for certain sections of the public, particularly the younger, ideological generation, and faded away under the harsh reality, leaving behind a spattering of dogmatic tittle-tattle and lots of bitter memories.

The aspiration to move from proletariat dictatorship to democratic expropriation was strong among the left-outs of the great socialist revolutions. Democracy became the buzzword, a tool which would supposedly offer the same sweet fruit without the associated thorn. Gamal Abdel Nasser of Egypt called his dictatorial regime 'presidential democracy', General Ayub Khan of Pakistan formulated 'basic democracy' for legitimacy, Sukarno of Indonesia devised 'guided democracy', Alfredo Stroessner of Paraguay legitimised his 35-year long rule with 'selective democracy' and many countries adopted a democratic veneer, such as autocratic North Korea which called itself the 'Democratic People's Republic of Korea' and so forth. The appellation 'democracy' became a touchstone for legitimacy, regardless of whether or not there is any semblance of democratic tit-bits in the country.

Nearly 50 years on, right wing fanatics and extremists seized on this opportunity to grab power through the democratic veneer. Once in power, by hook or by crook, clutching the touchstone of 'democracy', this power becomes almost invincible; no popular movement or ideology would dare touch it. Such is the magic of democracy.

The xenophobic opportunistic and racist views such as – 'America first', 'Brazil first', 'Philippines first' etc., are sweeping across the world. Whereas in the communism-socialism rounds, there was at least some semblance of social care, workers' rights etc; now in the right-wing extremism all those things have become peripheral and have been contemptuously dispensed with. The veneer of 'democracy' is only required to get to power, and the rest becomes superfluous.

The word 'democracy' originated from the Greek word 'demokratis', which is an amalgam of demos (mob, the many) and kratos (the rule). Thus, the original word signifies the 'rule of the many'. The Greek philosophers Socrates and then Plato along with his disciples had high hopes in democracy. Aristotle looked at various forms of governance over the centuries and gradually the consensus view emerged that the democratic participation of citizens as equals would ensure a free and fair form of governance; where rights, liberty and freedom of the people would be preserved.

But there were many shortcomings and apprehensions in that form of 'democracy', which Plato pointedly brought out. He asserted that the democratic system might lead to the establishment of the view of the majority, but that might not encompass the view of the whole or a large fraction of society. He particularly did not like the connotation of 'rule' over the whole society. Wouldn't that 'rule' by the majority mean the tyranny of the majority? And what form or type of 'rule' would be applicable over the whole society?

A true 'democracy' is something that may offer good governance, political justice, liberty, equality and human rights. Of course, not all of them can be fulfilled at the same time. But the majority of these attributes can be met with the majority of society. And the concept of 'rule' can be kept in abeyance, as it inherently means dictation over society.

The more important point is the 'issue' (the choice of government; a matter of national interest in a referendum etc.) on which the consensus of society is sought. Has the 'issue' been brought to the attention of the public with its pros and cons explained truthfully? In other words, are the public sufficiently knowledgeable or suitable to pass their opinion on the 'issue'?

The outcome would be blatantly distorted if people are ignorant or misinformed or misled with different or conflicting interpretations of the same issue. There are plenty of opportunistic populist politicians in this country and around the world who are ready to manipulate the situation to gain the support of the majority and gain power. This practice constitutes a blatant abuse of 'democracy'. It is very easy to mislead the public with convenient lies. Winston Churchill said, *"The best argument against democracy is a five-minute conversation with the average voter."*

Contrary to the conventional 'democratic principle', Roman Republicanism advocated that not everyone was fit to vote to elect the government. It gave some very good reasons including stating that only those who participate actively in public life and affairs of the State are qualified to vote. This ruling is eminently more sensible than allowing everybody to express opinions on issues regardless of their knowledge or suitability or association.

For example, a significant majority of the general public with very little or no knowledge of the role or functioning of the EU voted in the EU referendum on 23 June 2016 to leave and then on the following day more than one million people carried out a Google search on what 'EU' means! Their expressed opinion against the EU the previous day was not based on knowledge or rational assessment, but on prejudice and ignorance. Car workers throughout Britain voted overwhelmingly to leave Europe, because they were unhappy with their working conditions (nothing to do with the EU). The farmers in Wales and in large parts of England voted to leave on misinformation and false promises by Populist politicians. The general public were fed blatant lies that the NHS would get an extra £350 million per week on leaving the EU and there were many more lies. All of this misinformation and these blatant lies had fundamentally altered the knowledge base on which the public had voted and hence the outcome became skewed.

David Gauke, the Justice Secretary of the UK at that time, said on 3rd July 2019 in his Mansion House dinner speech, *"A willingness by politicians to say what they think the public want to hear, and a willingness by large parts of the public to believe what they are told by populist politicians, has led to a deterioration in our public discourse."* He also said, *"This has contributed to a growing distrust of our institutions – whether that be parliament, the civil service, the mainstream media or the judiciary."*

Democracy cannot survive in ignorance, illiteracy or moral degeneracy. When honesty, integrity, morality and ethics are divorced and opportunism and bigotry make inroads, democracy takes leave. As Franklin D. Roosevelt famously said, *"Democracy cannot succeed unless those who express their choice are prepared to choose wisely. The real safeguard of democracy, therefore, is education."*

Inevitable inequality in Capitalism

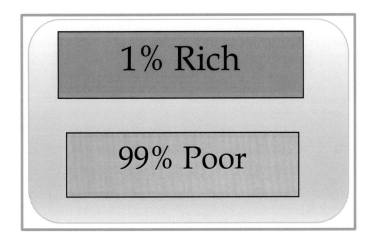

Figure 2.10   The rich/poor divide in America

With the demise of socialism in the Soviet Union over 30 years ago, the world of capitalism is having a field day now. Not that capitalism was constrained even in those days of a bipolar world, but there was some element of caution arising from political restraint and imperatives. But now those political restraints on capitalism have disappeared completely due to the voluntary embracement of capitalism by the erstwhile communist and socialist countries of the world. Capitalism is the only game in town now. Although China remained insular to the metamorphosis of the Soviet Union, it has accepted capitalism of its own volition. It is said that China is the largest and most ardent capitalistic society in the world today, leaving the previously ardent advocate and vigorous player — the United States of America — trailing far behind.

Capitalism, like communism or socialism, has its vices and virtues and which of these opposing traits becomes prominent at any one time depends on how it is practised in a particular country. Whereas communism or socialism requires a dictatorship (of the proletariat), capitalism can live quite happily with a pseudo-democratic system. Nonetheless, capitalism has shown to be more enduring than communism or socialism. Capitalism also has the pretension that it holds the high moral ground offering equal opportunities to all; it allows meritocracy, not autocracy to flourish. How far these egregious claims can be sustained in practice remains to be seen.

A recent book by Thomas Piketty, Professor of Economics at the Paris School of Economics, on *Capital in the Twenty-First Century*, published by Harvard University Press, has given an in-depth look at the world of capitalism on a historic basis and assessed its wide-ranging outcome. The book was published in March 2014 and has been one of the bestsellers in the Western world for a number of years. This weighty book spanning over 640 pages deals head on with the innate properties of capitalism – the most important of which is the creation and perpetuation of inequality in wealth.

Wealth has the intrinsic property of following itself and the reverse is also true, i.e. the deprivation of wealth is also perpetual! These tendencies can be described in everyday language as the rich become richer and the poor become poorer. This is the core outcome of the capitalistic economic system and Piketty articulates it very effectively. It must be stressed at the outset that this tendency of accumulation and deprivation of wealth, as depicted by Piketty, is all based on the free and fair transfer and transaction of capital. The illegal acquisition of wealth as is prevalent in developing countries, including Bangladesh, was left outside his discourse. The simple fact is that illegal possession follows no basic rule — a man can become a multi-millionaire overnight outside the practices of the economic system or he can lose his wealth overnight by a reverse process.

128

Also, if corruption becomes institutionalised, as is claimed in Bangladesh, the normal rules of the capitalistic system become totally irrelevant.

But before going any further, one needs to have a basic understanding of wealth and income. Wealth comes mainly from two sources – inherited wealth and wealth generated through income. Income in its turn is derived from two sources: earned income from labour (wages, salaries, bonuses, consultancy works etc.) and unearned income from capital (rents, interests, dividends, royalties, capital gains etc.). Capital may be considered as the total wealth owned at a given point in time, whereas income is a fluid quantity based on the economic performance of an endeavour. Capital and income are two quantities which may quantify the economic performance of an individual or the nation.

Capitalism does not differentiate between individuals, institutions or the government. Capital may be owned by an individual and/or by the government. The amount of available capital of an individual is the monetary value of the asset minus debt. The amount of capital in any nation is the sum total of individual capitals minus individual debts, plus national capital minus national debt. Obviously national capital and income are based on the aggregation of statistical evaluation of individuals' capital and income. In many countries, individuals evade tax and accumulate wealth (illegally). Consequently, the government loses revenue and has to borrow more money (quite often at the international money market) and runs a large national debt in order to run the country – maintain national defence, education, healthcare, transport etc. As a consequence, the country as a whole becomes poorer with large debts, but individuals may become inordinately rich. This is the trend in most, if not all, of the developing countries including Bangladesh. This trend is also discernible in many corrupt Western countries.

When income is obtained, it can either be saved or spent. But the most plausible outcome is that a part of it is spent and a part

129

is saved. If more income is saved than spent, then there is an accumulation of capital. On the other hand, if more is spent than saved, there is a dissipation of capital. The ratio of capital (net wealth) to income is a very good indicator of individual and/or national economic health.

On a national basis, the capital/income ratio indicates how national wealth if distributed per se would look like. In developed countries, as Piketty has pointed out, this ratio is between 5 and 6. What this means is that the average wealth of an individual is about 5 to 6 times higher than the average national income. If capital increases (due to the accumulation of capital and thereby benefitting from better returns) and the incomes of the masses get depressed, the ratio tends to go higher and that indicates that there is an unequal distribution of wealth.

What Piketty has shown is that the concentration of wealth and accumulation of capital to capital-rich individuals is an intrinsic property of capitalism. For example, if the rate of return on capital is higher than the economic growth of the nation (the economic growth of the nation is captured by the increase in income), there is an accumulation of capital. It is almost always the case that the rate of return on capital – roughly 5 per cent or even higher, depending on risk tolerance – is always higher than the economic growth of a nation, which varies between 1 to 3 per cent in the developed countries. There are times when the developed countries struggle to achieve even 1 per cent economic growth – for example, after the 2008 banking crisis, the average economic growth in the Western world was less than 1 per cent until very recently. Even now, when Britain is enjoying a high growth rate of about 3 per cent economic growth and the EU and America are growing by 2 per cent or so, and capital can easily grow at 5 per cent or more, thus the capital/income ratio is growing inexorably higher.

History shows that capital/income ratio in the developed world was between 5 and 6 in most of the 20th century, except during the two world wars and the inter-war period. During the wars, the capital of the nation diminished due to destruction of wealth and thereby the ratio dropped. For example, before the onset of WWI the ratio in Britain and France was in the range of 6 to 7; but after the war it was just around 3. The same effect can be discerned during WWII and its aftermath in both Europe and America. At the moment the ratio is between 5 and 6 in the developed world.

The capital/income ratio gives the wealth of a nation. The higher the ratio, the wealthier the nation or individuals of the nation. In general, a country with a high capital/income ratio (hence a wealthier nation) does not necessarily have an equitable distribution of wealth; in fact, just the reverse can be found to be true – there is more inequality in wealth distribution. This trend is inherent in capitalism. However, in some countries, such as Scandinavian countries, there are a high tax burden and generous social benefits – free medical facilities, free education, generous pensions etc. Even then, the inherent trend of capitalism could not be reversed. In other countries where social engineering is not practised vigorously, the inequality becomes even more pronounced. Let us consider the ownership of national wealth by individuals in various countries.

In Scandinavian countries where wealth is most equitably distributed (when compared to other countries) the richest 10 per cent own around 55 per cent of national wealth. In Britain, France, Germany and Italy, the richest 10 per cent own around 60 per cent of national wealth and the poorest 50 per cent around 5 percent. In France, as per 2010-2011 national data, the richest 10 per cent own 62 per cent of wealth and the poorest 50 per cent only 4 percent. In the United States, the distribution of wealth is even more skewed. The top 10 per cent own the staggering 72 per cent of wealth and the bottom 50 per cent a mere 2 per cent! Even these data are self-reported which has the undeniable fingerprints that a large amount of the fortunes of the wealthy may have been understated or underestimated. In fact, underestimation of wealth by the super-rich is almost a certainty when capital can easily be transferred to tax havens with no possibility of tracing it back to the hiding place by the Inland Revenue.

All of these mendacious activities leave the unmistakable fingerprints that the capitalist system is designed to give an unfair advantage to the rich. In addition, the system has been deliberately trimmed so that the poor are made to pay for the rich so that the rich become even richer – the banking crises just a few years back bear testimony to that. Even when a bank loses money, the bank bosses help themselves with mouth-watering annual bonuses. These banks, the epitome of the capitalist system, know very well that they are in business only because the poor sacrificed their money to rescue them. The then Bank of England Governor, Mark Carney, very eloquently presented his view at the City Conference in London recently that there was a growing sense that the basic social contract at the heart of capitalism was breaking down amid rising inequality.

Is Orwellian dystopia coming true?

The dire theme of Orwellian dystopia was that there could be a super-state that could carry out intrusive surveillance on all activities of its citizens and oversee the lives of individuals for its own purposes. Civil liberty, privacy, data protection etc. would be effectively superfluous terms with no real connotation – just utopian terms to satisfy the hyperbolic ego of the public. That day when the presumed Orwellian dystopia would come to be a reality is not too far off.

India has already completed a biometric database of nearly 90 per cent of 1.3 billion people of the country using fingerprints, iris scans and still photographs. The remaining 10 per cent or so will be completed soon. Logistically it was a super-daunting task covering such a huge population over the huge country, but they have nearly completed that task in a cost-effective way and the system is in operation. No matter where an Indian could be in the vast sprawling country, his 12-digit ID will uniquely identify who he is, where he comes from, what his occupation is etc., with a click of a button.

China, on the other hand, is going one step further and in a somewhat different direction. They are going for facial recognition. Whereas fingerprints, iris scans etc., are intrusive and legally these items belong to the individual who offered them in the first place; a facial image is public property - it is there for everyone to see and does not belong to any individual. The image can be taken without the individual even knowing about it and can be used without violating proprietary rights.

The idea of facial recognition by technological means came from the simple fact that human eyes can recognise faces of individuals with the blink of an eye. If human eyes can recognise human faces so easily and accurately, surely technologically it would be possible to do the same, even if the population size of human faces is enormous. The human face obviously carries all

133

the information that a photograph carries such as facial shape, colour of the skin, size of the eyes, nose etc; but in addition, it carries a host of other intrinsic information.

Human faces convey a multitude of subtle and not so subtle information. Emotions such as liking and disliking, anger and elation, love and hate, hope and despair, and even attempts of deceit and falsification are all etched on faces. The visual computation with a properly framed algorithm associated with artificial intelligence (AI) can effectively catch all of these emotional traits far more reliably than simple human eyes. If that is the case, then this facial recognition technique can presumably lead the human society to the dystopic state which Orwell feared so much.

A Chinese company in Beijing by the name Megvii (meaning mega-vision in Chinese) is spearheading this facial recognition technology in the field of human identification. A good quality video camera can take photos of individuals and then those photos are analysed with proper algorithms to decipher the requisite information. If a national data bank is available, then this simple innocuous photo can dig out the details of that individual – his name, address, family background, employment, his vehicle, driving records etc. Literally his whole background can be flashed out on the screen from a simple photo of his face.

Of course, there would be attempts to mislead or thwart this recognition technology by camouflaging the face with makeup or to cover part of the face with reflective sunglasses etc. But already research is going on to overcome the subversion of this facial recognition. The University of Cambridge had demonstrated that AI can reconstruct facial structures of people in disguise. So, there is nowhere to hide, the Big Brother will get you!

The potentiality of this start-up company is so great that within a short span of six years (it started in 2011), it is already valued at about $2 billion and 300,000 companies and individuals around the world are using this face recognition technology. Although visual recognition technology is not as advanced as speech recognition technology, it is making progress in leaps and bounds. In a few years' time, it may improve like the speech recognition with reliability improvement from 90% to 95% and then on to 99% and then facial recognition will take over the whole landscape of personal identification.

The smartphones are racing for reliable face recognition after the speech recognition of Amazon Echo. A couple of years ago, iPhone X unveiled a version of mobile technology where the owner's face can be recognised and used to unlock the device even in the dark. There are smartphones in China where the owners swipe their faces to authorise bank payments! In the UK Lloyds Bank is looking into facial recognition for ATM money withdrawal.

There are other advantages too. With terrorism and individual violence on the way up, there is a need to have surveillance across the whole spectrum of the society. Face recognition in areas such as train stations, tube/tram stations, bus stations, shopping malls etc. would be a vital tool to the security services. Even more important would be this technology at the airports. If someone is hatching a plot to blow up a plane, visual technology can discover his inner scheme and stop the scheme.

But Orwellian dystopia cannot be dismissed outright. Obviously, this technology when fully developed will have beneficial use, but the detrimental side of it cannot be ignored – it will embrace the whole society, it will go against the grain of civil liberty etc. So, a compromise has to be struck and that compromise would be dependent on the attitude of the state. A totalitarian state may use it purely to control its population for its own purpose, whereas a utopian state may use it purely for the safety and security of its population. A coin has always two sides.

The passing away of Mandela

Figure 2.11   Nelson Mandela, reverentially called Madiba (the father)

Nelson Mandela, the icon of freedom, forgiveness and reconciliation, was one of the brightest stars of the 20th century's humility, decency and civility. He passed away peacefully at his home in Johannesburg, South Africa on Thursday, December 5, 2013, aged 95. In breaking the news, South African President Jacob Zuma said, *"We have lost our greatest son."* On his death now, as much as during his lifetime, this iconic figure is held in almost universal respect and reverence right across the world – from Beijing to Buenos Aires, from Siberia to South Africa. There was hardly any newspaper on the day of his departure, anywhere in the world, which did not carry the sad news of passing away of this great man.

He was great, not because he ruled over a powerful nation on Earth, far from it. He took over the reign of a broken nation – a nation deeply torn and traumatised by decades of visceral racial hatred, institutionalised as an administrative policy called *apartheid* – and fixed it and made it to work so elegantly that within one term of his presidency (1994 – 1999) the nation was at peace with itself. Of course, there were problems in South Africa when he finished his presidency. But the country did not tear itself apart after decades of vicious racial segregation and violence. The blacks, the whites, the browns and any other inter-racial human beings called him, with utmost respect and reverence, the *Madiba* meaning the father.

The story of Nelson Mandela is as fascinating and inspiring as a fairy tale. He was born on 18th July 1918 as Rolihlahla Mandela. He was adopted as a foster child by a tribal chief in a remote South African town Mvezo, in the Eastern Cape and was raised in the tribal tradition. However, when he was sent to school, he had to change his name to Nelson Mandela as it was customary for school children to have English names. After finishing school, he started working in a law firm in Johannesburg and qualified as a lawyer in 1952. He joined the African National Congress (ANC) in 1944 as a show of protest against racial discrimination and repression. He was the first black lawyer to start a law firm and that was against the apartheid policy at that time. (Readers may be reminded here that another black lawyer by the name of Mohandas Karamchand Gandhi (Mahatma Gandhi) was thrown out of a first-class compartment in the same country some 50 years earlier, although he had a first class train ticket!)

In no time, Mandela had the inevitable brush with the authorities. He faced various restrictions here and there in his career as a lawyer. Ultimately, he was arrested in 1956 and charged with treason along with 155 other ANC members. The trials lasted for over four years and eventually they were acquitted in 1960. In 1962 he was again arrested and in 1963, when he was in prison, he was charged along with seven others with sabotage. In 1964 he was sentenced along with others to life imprisonment and sent to Robben Island prison.

In his memoir, *Long Walk to Freedom,* he describes his life (or lack of it) very succinctly; but strangely there was no feeling of anger or revenge. When he described the harshness of treatment and punishment, it was with total passivity and magnanimity. From 1964 till February 1990, he spent almost 27 years in a cell about 7ft long by 6ft wide. He used to sleep along the 7ft part of the cell, even then his head and toes used to touch the walls. He was not given any book or even allowed to read any newspaper during the early years of his imprisonment. One day, while he was outside the building to collect his meal, he found a page of newspaper lying on the courtyard. He picked it up and as nobody was shouting at him, he put the paper in his shirt pocket and came to his cell. Without waiting for the guards to go away, he opened the newspaper and started reading it – as he put it, *"like a child getting a candy".* He was so absorbed in reading the newspaper that he missed the sound of the guards' footsteps and all of a sudden, he heard two guards standing in front of him and saying, *" Mandela, we are charging you for unlawful possession of a newspaper and reading it."* The punishment he received was three days solitary confinement (in an even smaller cell!) with no food. The only thing he received there was rice water, which was the boiled water drained out of cooked rice.

However, as time passed, international protests - particularly among students throughout the whole world - grew louder and louder. In London Tariq Ali, the fiery left-wing students' leader, along with Peter Hain, a noted anti-apartheid campaigner (who subsequently became a Labour MP and Northern Ireland's Secretary of State and now Lord Hain) and others spent endless hours in Hyde Park Corner in the 1970s campaigning for the British government to impose sanctions against the *apartheid regime* in South Africa and to force that regime to release Nelson Mandela. There were vigorous campaigns not only in British campuses but also around the world. Although sanctions were imposed in 1967, they were ineffectual. While students were up in arms, conservative governments in the early 1980s in Britain

139

under Margaret Thatcher and in the United States under Ronald Reagan branded Nelson Mandela a terrorist!

However, under pressure, Western countries did impose severe sanctions and gradually the apartheid regime started to fall apart. In 1990, FW de Klerk lifted the ban on the ANC and on 11 February 1990, Nelson Mandela was released after nearly 27 years in prison. Nelson Mandela declared, *"We have, at last, achieved our political emancipation. Never, never and never again shall it be that this beautiful land will again experience the oppression of one by another."*

In 1993, Nelson Mandela was awarded the Nobel Peace Prize jointly with FW de Klerk. He described in his memoir quite succinctly that he was asked by many ANC leaders whether he should receive the Nobel Prize with FW de Klerk, the last apartheid-era president. He dismissed their disapproval by saying that when a person acknowledged the gross injustice he and the system had meted out to others, there was nothing more one could seek. The Nobel committee cited, *"their work for the peaceful termination of the apartheid regime, and for laying the foundation of a new, democratic South Africa."* Accepting the award, Nelson Mandela said, *"We will do what we can contribute to the renewal of our world."*

In 1994, because of Mandela's life-long struggle for justice, the people of South Africa, comprising all races and creeds, for the first time in its history got the democratic rights to vote. In the election, the ANC won and Nelson Mandela became the first black President in the post-apartheid era. White rule came to an end after more than three centuries in South Africa and Mr. Mandela was very gracious in acknowledging the tremendous contribution Mr. FW de Klerk made in bringing about this reconciliation.

What would be the legacy of Nelson Mandela? He is the epitome of forgiveness and reconciliation. But for him, South Africa could have been in a state of racial violence and internecine conflict. He defused the extremely volatile situation and brought the multi-racial protagonists to live in harmony and in peace. That is by no means a small achievement. One only needs to look around now to appreciate how difficult it is to bring two antagonistic parties, two different religious groups, or two different individuals together and live side by side amicably with honour and dignity.

It is amazing to note that two of the greatest men of the twentieth century – Nelson Mandela and Mahatma Gandhi – had so much in common. Both of them were lawyers by profession and both in their early lives suffered pain and suffering, abuses and injustice, strangely in the same country. Probably such pain and suffering made them what they were – to see clearly the inhumanity and injustice of the whole system – and that made them rise up and do something superhuman. Nelson Mandela was called Madiba and Gandhi was called Bapu – both meaning father in local languages! They were never vindictive, bore no grudges against anybody and by sheer force of humanity, sense of fairness and forgiveness they corrected and rectified nearly irreconcilable situations. So, it is no wonder that Nelson Mandela is dubbed with very good justification as the Gandhi of South Africa.

The Illusion of Reality

Reality is considered to be the state of a thing or a situation, not a notional idea or perception, that is unambiguously or obviously present at a specific space and time. The state of reality is vivid, transparent and beyond doubt. A 'real' thing is there, right in front of the eyes of the beholder to observe with full consciousness. But is reality as 'real' as it is claimed to be? Is there no illusion in viewing or observing something that is 'real'?

Nearly a century ago (1930 to be precise), Tagore, '*the poet with the head of a thinker*', and Einstein, '*the thinker with the head of a poet*', debated (and some would say, clashed) on the nature of reality at Einstein's home outside Berlin. Einstein held the notion of reality that was vivid, transparent, visible, for example, 'the moon was there, whether one looked at it or not', 'beauty was there, whether one observed it or not'. Reality arises from physical presence that cannot be denied or disputed.

On the other hand, Tagore held the view that the reality of all physical objects, truth, beauty and so forth was dependent on human consciousness. Without human consciousness, the reality of anything was incoherent and irrelevant. He maintained that this world was a human world – the scientific view of it was also that of a scientific man. Therefore, the world without us does not exist, it is a subjective world, depending for its reality upon our consciousness.

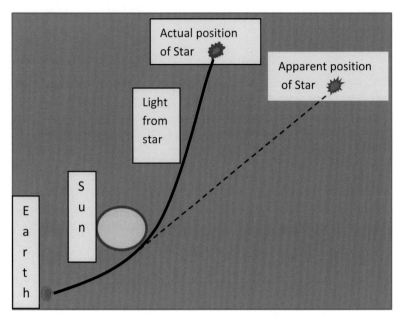

Figure 2.12   Reality may be misleading

Even in scientific parlance, reality is not always 'real' as we view it; it can deceive our perception, our senses and consciousness; or the sense of reality may be partial or incomplete. Let us look at the figure given above. The light from a distant star can be bent by the gravitational field of the Sun before it reaches us and then we view the position of the star at its 'apparent position'. Of course, with scientific investigation, taking other parameters into consideration, the 'real' position of the star can be accurately determined. But to a common man, the 'apparent position' is the 'real' position of the star, he can point it out in the sky with his own fingers and that is the reality for him!

The moon is the nearest celestial body from Earth. Even then, what we see or do not see of the moon may not be the real thing. For example, we may not see the moon due to cloud cover, but that does not mean the moon is not there in the sky. In Islam, religious events are fixed by the sight of the moon and the lack of sight of the moon does not mean that the moon is not there in reality. That illusion of absence is taken as a substitute for reality. The light we get from our nearest star, beyond the Sun, comes to us four years after it has been emitted. In other words, our reality of that star is four years behind the present time. We can get light or radiation from a star or a galaxy some 100 million or 200 million or 1000 million years from us, as they are so many light years away from us, and during that time that star or galaxy may have died or disappeared. So, our reality of the existence of that star could be totally out of place.

The nearer an object is from us, the more accurate is our perception of the reality of that object. However, on the miniscule scale of the atomic and sub-atomic realm, i.e. the quantum field, our reality takes another knock. In there, particles like electrons, quarks etc., take on the dual role of particles and waves - which one at which point no one knows. An electron whizzes around the nucleus of an atom as waves, but when an energy is given to it or taken away from it, it behaves like a particle. Only the act of observation can determine the true nature or the reality of the electron. In quantum mechanics, it is axiomatic that only in the act of observation does an electron become real. An unobserved electron is unreal (Copenhagen interpretation).

However, an observed electron does not behave exactly the same way in various circumstances. A concrete example is the double slit experiment when electrons are fired one at a time and an interference pattern is observed on the screen due to the wave nature of electrons. Now, if a detector is placed to detect which slit the electron is going through, the interference pattern disappears. If the detector is then switched off, leaving all other arrangements intact, the interference pattern reappears. It is as if the electron does not like to be detected which way it is going. In other words, the act of observation modifies the outcome and the reality.

145

The view of reality in the cosmological scale may be misconstrued, as objects may not be exactly where they apparently appear to be (see the above figure). Also, in the ultra-small sub-atomic fields, objects cannot be assigned any particular positions based on physical principles. Only an act of observation may offer the object a specific position and that may be construed as the reality. But strangely, that act of observation may change the otherwise reality!

Over the centuries and millennia, people have been narrating different 'real' stories. Moses, the prophet of Judaism, saw a bushfire in the cornfield right in front of his eyes and when he went nearer, that bushfire disappeared, he saw nothing was burnt and received God's command not to approach it any further. To him, the event was vivid and real (although we now know that he witnessed a mirage). To George W Bush, the command from God to invade Iraq was real (unless he made it up). To millions of fanatic religious people, the existence of God or Allah or Yahweh is absolute and real; heaven and hell are real. It is the state of their mind that dictates reality.

Thus, there does not seem to be a universal notion or narrative of a reality that is true to everyone on every occasion. Reality seems to be subjective, depending on an individual's state of mind or consciousness, as Tagore had asserted. What is real, vivid and utterly true to someone may be totally unrealistic, utterly non-sensical to another person with a different state of mind. Reality can thus be an illusory notion.

World population and environmental catastrophe

We are all aware of, indeed seriously concerned about, climate change and global warming. The large majority of scientists – environmentalists, climatologists, atmospheric physicists, geophysicists, geochemists, oceanographers and experts of hosts of associated disciplines – as well as the overwhelming proportion of the human population, unanimously hold the view that significant climate change is indeed taking place and that is all due to human activities. But then a small but powerful section of the population, mostly in America, rejects this contention and assigns changes to just natural activities. Obviously, these people have vested interests in deflecting away human activities.

It is blatantly obvious that human activities are the root causes of climate change. Of course, nature may be reacting to adverse conditions created by human beings, but the initial cause is human activity. One may ask, why is it that Earth is reacting so catastrophically over the last few decades when it existed in stable conditions for thousands of years? The answer is undoubtedly *'WE ARE THE CAUSE'*, there are too many of 'US' – the human beings on the surface of the Earth demanding, exploiting and extracting Earth's resources ruthlessly without any regard to its stability, sustainability and interconnectedness.

Some 200 years ago or even 100 years ago we were doing what we are doing now – spewing out carbon dioxide and other global warming gases into the atmosphere – but that did not change climatic conditions irreversibly, because not enough of us had been doing the damaging actions. But now more than 7,500 million of us abusing the Earth have probably pushed the Earth to the threshold of, or beyond, its sustainability.

The large human population of the present day is causing the problems. The United Nations' estimation of human population from 1050 CE to 2017 CE is shown in Figure 2.13, where the past numbers have been compiled from human records and best estimate values. At no time until 1850 CE has the global human population exceeded 1.0 billion. Around 1750 CE, when the Industrial Revolution took place, the Western world started using coal and other fossil fuels to improve living conditions and consequently the population started to grow significantly. From that time on, improvements, not only in the standards of living, started to take place but also better hygiene and improved medical conditions managed to bring down the death rate and thereby helped to increase population growth. At the moment the global population is 7.5 billion and growing at the rate of 80 million every year and this number is also growing. Since 1970, the global population had gone up by two-fold!

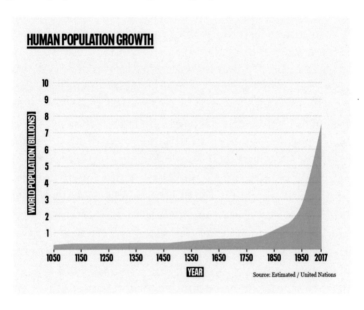

Figure 2.13 Human population from 1050 to 2017

In the 1960s and 1970s there were intense debates about the sustainability of the world population beyond about 3.5 billion, particularly with regard to food production. As estimated at that time, in about 12 to 15 years the population will grow by more than a billion (about 30% of the prevailing population). If so, could food production be increased by about 30% in that time scale? The global population has been going up at that rate ever since despite all the measures taken to curtail it.

As the population grows, there are extra demands for housing and other socio-economic facilities and a consequent reduction of arable land. But human ingenuity prevailed – multiple crop production, better yielding crops, crop rotation, disease-resistant seeds and now *GM* crops etc., – have improved food production. In fact, food production has improved so much that food supply for the population is no longer an issue. But that has created additional serious problems, particularly environmental problems, which need to be tackled.

The United Nations have also produced a population growth projection for the years 1950 to 2100, as shown in Figure 2.14. Many factors affect population growth and incorporating various assumptions in those factors produce widely varying outcomes. The middle thick green line is the outcome based on best estimate values, whereas the top and bottom lines are those with a 95% level of confidence in various assumptions. If corrective actions such as proper family planning, better education and social responsibility of the population etc., are taken, the population growth could be limited to 9.6 billion in 2100, whereas unbridled growth will show a figure of 13.6 billion. The difference between two extremes in population numbers in 2100 is about 4 billion, more than 50% of the present population. That is an alarming prospect indeed.

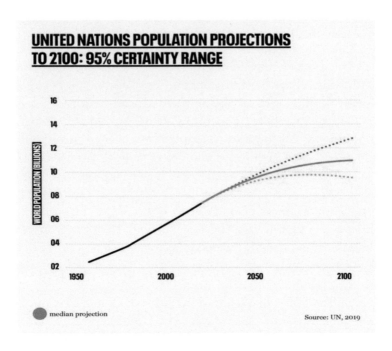

Source: UN, 2019

Figure 2.14 Human population projection until 2100

Population distribution is not uniform round the world, as shown in Figure 2.15. At the moment over 60% (4.6 billion) of the world population is in Asia, and Africa has less than 20% (1.5 billion) population. But by 2100 the Asian population may remain the same or even decline, whereas the African population will shoot up to 4.4 billion, more than three times the present population. This drastic increase will place an enormous burden on the continent and may even lead to violent responses, unprecedented population migration to other continents etc. This situation will arise on top of ensuing environmental deterioration – global warming, extreme weather conditions etc.

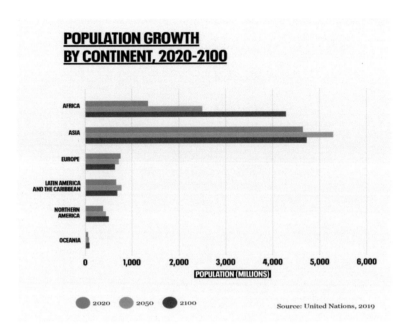

Figure 2.15   Population growth by continents

It is interesting to note that China's present population of over 1.42 billion would come down to about 1.06 billion by 2100, whereas India's population would grow from 1.35 billion to 1.46 billion in the same timescale, as shown in Figure 2.16. China's drastic reduction in population is due to lower fertility rates which arise due to the older population group. China has imposed a two-child policy right from its inception and gradually it is bearing fruit. Recently China has relaxed its two-child policy to counter the drop in national population, which has been more than it anticipated.

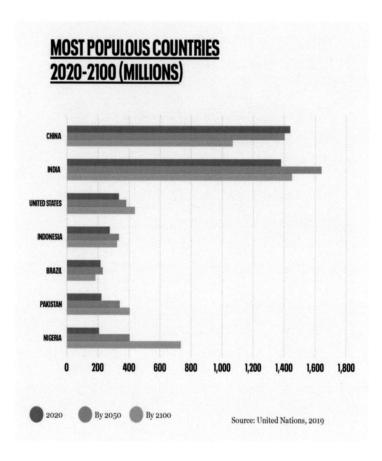

Source: United Nations, 2019

Figure 2.16   Most populous countries

As already mentioned, population growth is multifactorial. But a very important factor is the economic condition of the country. A runaway population growth stunts the economic growth of the country and at the same time a low economic growth tends to encourage higher population growth. A family tends to produce more children in a poverty-stricken country so that the children can look after the parents at their old age. Thus, population growth and poverty form a vicious circle. Examples are Pakistan and Nigeria where large population growths are anticipated. On the other hand, Bangladesh is the country which has broken out of this vicious circle.

Let us get back to the aforementioned theme that climate change is primarily due to the presence of a vast population. Coal extraction and its use by a limited number of people catering for one or two billion people in the Western world in the 18th or 19th century was not that damaging to the climate. But, as the deprived population of the East as well as other decolonised countries' populations are striving to improve living standards from abysmal depths, demand for natural resources like coal, gas and petroleum oil as well as minerals has gone up exponentially and environmental degradation has followed suit.

Nature has an inbuilt mechanism of correcting itself when there is any deviation or offset from the norm, which is commonly known as negative feedback. If there is an increase in temperature in the summer, more water from the sea would evaporate and subsequent rain would cool down the area. There are lots of factors acting in opposite phase to the initial condition to stabilise the natural conditions and that is the negative feedback.

But there may be situations when moderate negative feedback conditions could break down and violent responses would ensue. If due to an excessive increase in global temperature, Arctic and Antarctic ice caps melt, then there would be no seasonal cold stream of water, no moderation of summer temperature etc. In some areas, the temperature would become so high that there would be almost spontaneous fire – as in Australia, California and even in Siberia. Condensation would be restricted to limited areas giving a large increase in rainfall – as in England in 2018 - causing unprecedented floods etc.

So, either we pull ourselves back from the precipice by limiting and then reversing the damage that has already been inflicted to nature or we let nature go berserk threatening the very existence of human life, or for that matter, any form of life on earth.

Coronavirus - virus of the lungs and Meme - virus of the brain

We are in the throes of two strains of *virus* – one is the virus of lungs called coronavirus and the other is the virus of the brain called meme (similar to gene in biological speak). I will deal with these two viruses sequentially below and show that there are many commonalities, despite the fact that one is a biological virus and the other is a cultural virus.

Despite this dissimilarity, there are a lot of common traits – they both replicate, colonise or parasitize the respective organs of the human body; they both propagate through air from human body to human body and incubate within the host body for a while before they express themselves; when they express themselves, they destroy the host body and transmit the virus to other adjacent bodies; they cause tremendous damage to society, the economy, the education system and all other branches of civilised society. Worst of all, there are no known cures against them at the moment. They are so vicious that either humanity will kill them, or they will kill humanity.

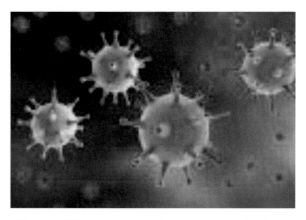

Figure 2.17   *Coronavirus – virus of the lungs*

155

So, what is this vicious coronavirus – also called *COVID-19* –
as a particular strain? It is a virus, which means that it is a
microscopic parasite that infects living organisms. It consists of a
nucleic acid molecule – typically *RNA* but it can also be *DNA* –
with a protein coat. It can replicate itself, like genes, within the
living cells. When it invades the specific organ – the lungs - of a
host body it spikes through the cell's membranes and gets inside
the cell and start replicating. It is speculated that this coronavirus
jumped from animals to the human species.

Obviously, the host cells do not like this invasion and their
defence mechanism (generally called the immune system) is put
into action and a battle ensues. While this battle is raging on
cellular levels in a specific organ, other organs are functioning
normally and the host body is completely unaware of the vicious
battle taking place within his or her body. This may take a few
days, which in the case of coronavirus is called incubation or the
dormant period. After three or four days of the battle, if not won
by the body's defence mechanism, it goes into all-out war against
the invading parasites. That is when the host body starts
showing some symptoms, like high temperature, coughing and
breathlessness etc. The fight goes on and depending on the
outcome, the patient can start recovering or go progressively
worse.

Although at the beginning there were no antidotes or
remedies against the invading viruses, recently developed
vaccines have given the body's defence mechanism some
assistance to fight off the virus. However, even with antidotes, it
is advised that social distance and personal hygiene be
maintained.

In the worst case, if the invading virus is on the verge of
victory and occupies the lungs creating pus in the alveoli sacs
and impeding breathing, then ventilation units can be used to
artificially supply oxygen to the body and keep the defence
system going to fight to the last. Quite often the body's defence

mechanism can beat off the invaders even at this stage and recover. This is the do or die stage. Altogether it is anticipated that it will take 14 days from initial invasion to full recovery.

The other virus – the virus of the brain which Richard Dawkins, Professor Emeritus of the University of Oxford and an evolutionary biologist, calls a meme to resemble gene – is equally, if not more, vicious and malicious as coronavirus. A meme is not a biological virus in the strict sense as coronavirus is. But it is a cultural virus behaving exactly like any other biological virus – replicating, propagating, colonising and eventually destroying the host body.

Memes carry a remarkable resemblance to genes. As genes propagate in the gene pool from body to body through sperm cells or egg cells, so do memes in the meme pool jumping from brain to brain of human beings through cultural imitation or peer pressure. It could sometimes be benign or not too intrusive, when there is just cultural imitation. A new designer dress or the latest mobile phone can take a 'must have' label to a group of people and that may take on obsessive space in the brain. The other example can be a catchy song or rhyme or a social media movement like 'Me Too', 'Black Lives Matter' etc., which may become obsessive mimicry. These are benign memes with hardly any damaging aspect.

But the real meme with an uncanny resemblance to a gene or virus is the parasite that colonises the brain obsessively. It can easily propagate from brain to brain, jump over cultural barriers, jump over national barriers and last for a long period of time. Take, for example, the *belief in life after death* - it is a meme that can easily parasitize brains and propagate across all social, political and cultural boundaries and there is no antidote to it. No rational argument or concrete evidence (similar to remedies against viruses) can be produced to counter that belief and hence this meme would flourish almost unhindered, even without any evidence supporting it.

157

Then there are other more gripping memes: the idea of God or Yahweh or Allah. This meme has been digging in human brains for almost 4,000 years through various religions, cultures, art and literature, music and social encounters. The existence of God is now taken as absolute without any shred of evidence supporting it. This is the most durable primary meme supporting other auxiliary memes like *life after death* or *heaven and hell* or *'hell-fire for the sinners'* etc. Each of these memes supports the other meme and together they stand strong, invincible, absolute and incontrovertible.

When a meme gets a strong foothold in the brain through continuous reinforcement, it comes as vivid as a gene or even stronger. In Islam, the first sound a newborn baby is supposed to hear is the prayer call for Allah. Admittedly, it is symbolic, but it is the symbol that will become real throughout the whole life. The first lesson a child gets is how to read Arabic and the Quran. A practising Muslim is supposed to have prayers five times a day in a mosque and each time he is reminded of the existence of God and his supreme power with the rhetorical question, "Who created the Earth"? With such persistent messages and unquestionable submission to God's authority by the Imam and fellow Muslims, it is quite normal that God and his divine presence become as vivid a meme in the brain as gene is in the cell.

Although memes are cultural imitation and analogues of biological genes, they are no less real and damaging than other viruses. In fact, when fanatic Muslims happily sacrifice their lives (i.e. their gene pool) for the messages carried through their memes (i.e. a guaranteed place in heaven for those who give up lives on Earth for God), then one must wonder what is more vivid and real: a gene or a meme? One can call an embedded meme a prejudice, but to the man who holds that prejudice, it is as real as the Sun and the Moon in the sky.

Albert Einstein said nearly a century ago, *"What a sad era, when it is easier to smash an atom than a prejudice."*

We are hurtling towards a disastrous climate change – Part I

The human race is staring into the abyss of unprecedented climate change of its own making. The clock of climate change is ticking remorselessly; it has gone past the 11th hour and, although not exactly on the 59th minute, is not too far from it. We pride ourselves to be civilised human beings, we claim unprecedented scientific and technical achievements; but we have failed miserably to realise the damage we have inflicted and are still inflicting on our planet. Our actions are anything but civilised. A large section of the human population under the guidance and influence of 'civilised political leaders' in many Western and Eastern countries is in complete denial of the climatic damage!

In order to appreciate how close we are to the tipping point of irreversible climate change, we need to look at the factors that initiate climate change. The term 'climate change' encompasses the totality of processes like the global warming, sea levels rising, the loss of polar ice caps, floods, fires, droughts and so forth. These processes do not take place haphazardly or arbitrarily for no reasons; there are deep-rooted causes for these effects.

The causes for these effects are multifarious. Causes range from emission of greenhouse gases from uncontrolled industrial activities, excessive exploitation of the Earth's resources, deforestation, the rise in human population, remorseless demands for improved standards of living, increased air travel etc. All these factors contribute to climate change due to enhanced greenhouse gas emission. And the quantity that is primarily used to characterise climate change is the increase in global temperature.

The root cause of the increase in temperature is the increase in greenhouse gas concentration in the Earth's atmosphere. A sort of runaway situation has arisen here. An increase in greenhouse gas leads to higher global temperature and higher global temperature leads to higher greenhouse gas. Unless decisive action is taken by human beings to arrest this situation, the human race is in peril.

The legitimate question that arises here is how can one assert that this rise in global temperature leading to climate change is mainly due to human activities, when both natural processes and human activities contribute to global temperature? That is a genuine question.

The planet Earth has undergone large climate swings over the millennia. Scientists have looked into these variations in Earth's climate over the past 650,000 years and have found that there has been as many as seven ice ages during this period and in between ice ages, which are called inter-glacial periods, there have been some warmer periods with an increase in global temperatures. Hominis (human species) had not evolved until about 250,000 years ago and so global temperatures could all be assigned to natural causes.

When nearly 250,000 years ago, Homo habilis emerged in the savannas of Africa, man started interacting with nature. But those primitive men had no way of exploiting the Earth; they were passive, subservient onlookers of nature.

Climatologists looked at the inter-glacial periods, i.e. between two cold glacial spells, and established a baseline temperature. After the baseline temperature was established, then any excess global temperature found over a period when human activity was known to have taken place can be assigned to human activities. This is an established scientific technique, and it is applied to many scientific fields to separate out human activities from natural activities.

The planet Earth is blanketed by a layer of gases in the outer atmosphere. This atmosphere containing a variety of gases allows solar radiation to come through but blocks out or shields harmful ionising radiation from the outer skies. A small fraction of solar energy is reflected back from Earth's surface to the outer skies. Normally if the atmosphere is unpolluted, this reflected energy in the form of infrared radiation would escape to outer space. On the other hand, if there are pollutants such as carbon dioxide, methane etc., this radiation is held back and reflected towards the Earth again. Thus, gradually excess energy is accumulated in the planet and its temperature goes up.

The types of gases that deter infrared radiation from escaping from Earth have been found to be carbon dioxide (CO_2), methane gas (CH_4), nitrous oxide (N_2O), chlorofluorocarbon (CFC) and a few more. Atmospheric concentrations of carbon dioxide in ppm (parts per million) and methane gas in ppm over the period 1500 CE to the present time have been estimated by scientists and presented in the graphs below. The period 1720 CE to 1800 CE is the Industrial Revolution period when human activities kicked in large scale. Before this industrialisation period, humans were living in harmony with nature. It can be seen from both of these graphs in Figure 2.18 that the Industrial Revolution was the prompt to initiate enhanced concentration which continued in accelerated fashion right up to the present day.

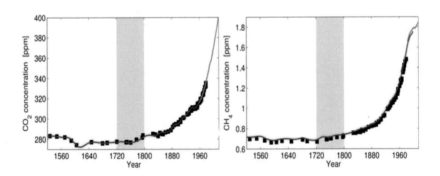

Figure 2.18   *CO_2 and CH_4 conc. From 1500 to 2000 CE (Courtesy: www.theconversation.com)*

Along with these two graphs, one should consider the rise in global temperature which is shown below in Figure 2.19. The similarity in the overall shape and pattern of these graphs is striking and one can draw the conclusion that they are correlated. It shows beyond doubt that the rise in temperature above the 1850 to 1900 (industrialisation period) baseline is due to increased concentration of global warming pollutants – CO_2 and CH_4. There are other significant pollutants such as chlorofluorocarbon (CFC), but they are not shown here.

The CO_2 concentration in the pre-industrialised period was between 200 to 270 ppm and Earth had a thermally stable period. But now this concentration has risen to about 350 ppm leading to about a 1°C rise in temperature. But, if the present trend continues, by the end of the present decade the temperature may well go up more than 1.5°C and that would bring in very harsh conditions for all forms of life on Earth.

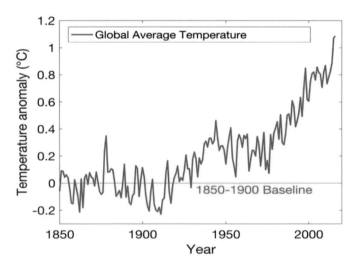

Figure 2.19   Global temperature from 1850 to 2020 CE. (Courtesy: www.theconversation.com)

164

From the 1970s, scientists have been saying that human beings were damaging Earth's atmosphere and its natural conditions and care should be taken to limit it or even reverse it. But political leaders of various persuasions, particularly Americans and those with vested interests dealing with fossil fuels, have kept denying any global warming or any climate change.

When confronted with increased severity and more frequent incidences of droughts, bushfires, floods, storms, cyclones, cold spells etc., these climate change deniers started saying that these are natural phenomena; nothing to do with human activities. Their denial is either based on ignorance or moral depravity.

Only a few countries holding such views are damaging the good work of a large number of countries. Donald Trump, immediate past president of America, is the most vociferous denier of all. America is one of the largest polluters, second only to China, in the world. By denying man-made causes, America can stop taking any action to reduce or eliminate greenhouse gas emission. Pursuing such damaging anti-global policy, America, under Donald Trump, withdrew from the Paris Agreement in 2017. However, Joe Biden, the present president of America, has immediately re-joined the Paris Agreement.

The Paris Agreement of 2015 aims to limit global warming to 1.5°C relative to a pre-industrial baseline. Its precise commitment is: *Holding the increase in the global average temperature to well below 2°C above pre-industrial levels and to pursue efforts to limit the temperature increase to 1.5°C above pre-industrial levels, recognising that this would significantly reduce the risks and impacts of climate change.*

We all live on the same planet. When one country, namely America, the second largest polluter, pursued policies under Trump to damage the planet environmentally, it effectively neutralised and negated the sacrifices made by many poorer nations of the world. What Trump did in America was not only morally repugnant but also globally outrageous.

We are hurtling towards a disastrous climate change – Part II

In Part I, it was shown unambiguously that human activities from the period of the Industrial Revolution (1720 – 1800) had been the root cause for the rise of global temperature by over 1°C due to emission of greenhouse gases into the atmosphere. As industrial activities became more and more widespread, the greenhouse gas emission and its accumulation in atmosphere increased accordingly and the global temperature went up even higher.

Climatologists, geoscientists, atmospheric scientists and so forth had been warning the world leaders of signs of increase in global temperature over and above the natural increase right from the early 1970s. As time passed, their warning became louder and louder, but the leaders of industrialised countries deliberately ignored them or rejected their scientific evidence. The United States of America is, in particular, the champion of such denial right from the beginning – presidents such as Ronald Reagan, George H W Bush, George W Bush and recently Donald Trump are all rejectionists of man-made global climate change.

Despite incontrovertible scientific principles and evidence that an increase in carbon dioxide (CO_2), methane (CH_4), nitrous oxide (N_2O), chlorofluorocarbon (CFC) and other gases in the atmosphere traps energy i.e. heat within Earth's atmosphere and thereby increases global temperature, the deniers reject all these arguments. Their short-sightedness and the damage they are inflicting on Earth are simply inexcusable.

The consequences of global increase in temperature are given below:

When air temperature increases, land surface temperature increases more than sea temperature, as the heat capacity of water is more than that of soil. What it means is that for the same amount of heat, water temperature will increase less (due to its high heat absorbing capacity) than that of soil. Similarly, when air temperature drops, the land temperature drop would be more than the sea temperature. Thus, sea temperature does not move up or down as much as the adjoining land mass temperature and that is why we get the moderating effect of the sea.

This land-sea temperature differential is also the cause of rain, storms, snowfall etc. In the summer, land temperature increases substantially causing air to rise to high altitude, and sea air being relatively cooler and heavier but laden with moisture moves towards land and gives rain. A higher temperature difference would give a higher amount of rain, higher wind velocity (storm, tornado etc.). Reciprocally, in the winter there would be severe snowfall, extreme cold spells etc. So, the climate change would exacerbate the nascent conditions.

Melting of inland glaciers around the world, which would then be followed by Antarctic and Greenland ice sheets melting, would cause the sea-level to rise significantly. It is not only the extra volume of water from melting ice but also the thermal expansion of water due to rise in temperature would cause sea-levels to rise and inundate large areas of land mass. It is estimated by the IPCC that by the end of this century, the sea-level is likely to rise by at least 6ft (or even higher), if no remedial action is taken now i.e. if life continues as 'business-as-usual'. But if action is taken urgently now to limit temperature rise to 1.5^0C, the sea-level rise may be contained within 3ft to 6ft.

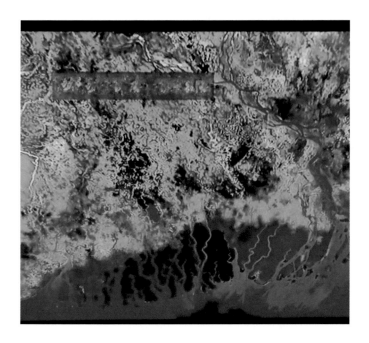

Figure 2.20   *Mangrove areas of Sundarbans in Bangladesh at present*

In addition to that, worsening storm surges, frequent tropical storms and concentrated rainfall will affect large coastal areas and even the inlands of a country, islands and low-lying areas. Bangladesh, a low-lying country, would be badly affected by sea-level rise. The average landmass there is only about 5ft above the sea level. Figure 2.20 shows the mangrove areas of Sundarbans in the southern part of the country at present and Figure 2.21 shows when the sea level rises by the smallest estimated margin of 3ft. It can be seen that large areas have been inundated by the rising sea level. It is estimated that 1.3 billion people world-wide would be affected, which may require their permanent relocation or even mass migration.

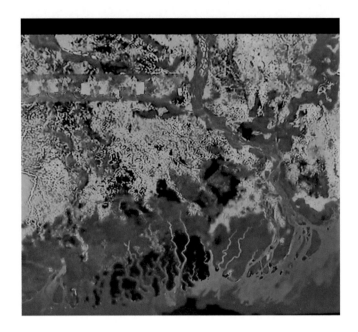

*Figure 2.21   Mangrove areas of Sundarbans in Bangladesh
anticipated to be around 2050 AD*

It may be pointed out that sea-level rise does not just cause submersion of landmass, which might have been a habitable area previously, but also damages arable land. Ingress of saline water from sea precludes cultivation of crops, vegetation etc., even in surrounding areas which are not inundated.

Thawing permafrost speeds up global warming, as permafrost is basically soil that stays below freezing (0^0C) for at least two years. Plants capture carbon dioxide (CO_2) from the atmosphere by the photosynthesis process and then this carbon is released when wood (in roots) decays in the soil or carbon is compressed in the natural process to form coal. In Arctic areas, wood decay or decomposition is very slow and hence these areas are regarded as carbon sink. However, decomposition increases as temperature increases causing enhanced carbon emission. The

170

inventory of frozen carbon in permafrost is 1.5 trillion tons, which is nearly twice the amount of carbon in the atmosphere now!

Wildfires are caused due to global warming, and these then contribute to further global warming. Wildfire thus has a positive (destructive) feedback effect. Trees and vegetation absorb CO_2 and convert it to oxygen (O_2), thus acting as sinks. Tropical forests in Indonesia, Malaysia, Brazil and in other parts of the world play a vital role in carbon sequestration. However, wildfires effectively convert the sink of carbon straight into a source of carbon! The forest fires that are raging in the Amazon rainforest now, which is regarded as the lungs of the planet Earth, are extremely damaging. These forest fires are not natural wildfires; these are deliberate man-made fires to clear forest areas for agricultural use. Man is making the planet uninhabitable.

The effect of all these changes is causing severe disruption to the climate. Where there were moderate rainfalls, now there are severe rainfalls causing flash floods, bursting of dams, landslides etc. In 2018, there were devastating floods in Japan, North Korea and India. In 2019, bridges in North Yorkshire, England collapsed when a full month's rain fell in just four hours.

While some parts of the world were having a tremendous amount of rainfall in a short spell of time, others were baking in heat waves. France's capital, Paris, experienced in June 2019 the highest temperature of 46°C and India experienced 50°C. Pakistan experienced a deadly heat wave where the highest recorded temperature was 54°C!

There were unprecedented wildfires in Greece and Australia. Wildfires in the forest area called Paradise in California are devastating and are becoming a regular event. Northern Finland (in the Arctic Circle) and Siberia were used to be considered so cold that wildfires were thought to be incredible, but not any more. Last year as well as this year, wildfires in those areas devastated a large land mass.

In the year 2017, hurricane Irma, a category 5 storm, was the most powerful Atlantic storm in a decade to strike the Caribbean and Southern US. In addition, hurricane Harvey in Texas and hurricane Maria in the Dominican Republic wrought havoc. Monsoon floods in Bangladesh and mudslides in Sierra Leone were devastating natural disasters in 2017.

The frequency and severity of these natural disasters are breaking all previous records. A natural disaster, which only 10 or 15 years ago would have been considered a once in 100 years event, is now happening once or twice a decade and if runaway conditions are allowed to continue, those events may become regular events.

Donald Trump not only denied man-made climate change but also encouraged activities which cause climate change. He and his right-wing coterie of extremist Republicans in America held and promoted the view that climate change was due to natural phenomena. There is an Institute in America, called the Heartland Institute (which Trump endorsed and supported) which claims to be one of the world's "leading free market think-tanks" and promotes "free market solutions to social, economic and environmental problems". It disputes scientific observations and knowledge on climate change (as is usual with right-wing cliques to denigrate scientific knowledge), criticises climate mitigation activities and promotes use of fossil fuels. With such 'free-market think-tanks' in countries like America, disastrous climate change can hardly be avoided.

When continents clash

It is not the collision of the tectonic plates that I am alluding to here or the drift of the continents towards each other, it is the mighty clash of dominant religions from the adjoining continents. The religion of Islam from the East (the Middle East and North Africa) crossed over to the West in Spain and clashed for centuries for dominance.

Spain was the battleground for two dominant religions vying for territorial gains. Islam from North Africa and north-west of the Middle East eyed Spain some twelve centuries ago as the gateway to Europe for religious expansion. Obviously, the dominant religion (Catholicism) of the region clashed, fought back and what happened during the next few centuries not only shaped Spain but also the whole of Europe.

Recently I travelled to 'Classical Spain' with Riviera Travels visiting places like Seville, Cordoba and Granada, among others, where Islam came, conquered and was eventually beaten back and relinquished the gains some centuries later in the face of relentless antagonism from the indigenous religions.

Our travel started when we landed at Malaga airport (a southern coastal city of Spain), when Riviera Travels grouped together tourists from Manchester and the south of England and brought them through Manchester and Gatwick airports. A drink reception in the evening was followed by a buffet dinner where we came to know other tourists. We spent the night at a 4-star hotel which was some 1,100 ft above sea level and hemmed in on the sloping banks of a hill overlooking the Mediterranean Sea.

Next morning, we travelled to Ronda, a small town on the outskirts of Sierra de Grazalema national park, trekking a scenic route past Marbella (a holiday resort famous for night clubs) and on the way managed to have a glimpse of Gibraltar across the sea. It is surprising that for such a desolate rocky mountainous outpost, two countries went to battles a number of times over the centuries. We spent nearly five hours in Ronda, which is famous for bull fighting, in particular. It is claimed that bull fighting started in Ronda, but other cities like Seville and Madrid would dispute that vehemently. After having fantastic mixed tapas for lunch, we went to see the 'new bridge' connecting two hill cliffs over a gorge of some four hundred feet drop. The sound of cascading water in the gorge below is soothing, but the sight of hundreds of feet of almost vertical drop is awesome. As I looked from the bridge down the gorge, I saw people trekking along the small stream meandering along the boulders, rocks and some tropical trees.

Another three hours of bus trip took us to the famous city of Seville. After checking in at the hotel at the centre of the city, we went to have 'tapas tasting' at a local restaurant (given free for Riviera travellers) and then after the dinner, we went to see the famous 'Mushroom Tower'. This 'Mushroom Tower' has a fascinating history. Some twelve years ago, Seville politicians had the bright idea of digging a tunnel across that area to construct a relief road. As they dug, they started getting more and more Roman artefacts and then they found a Roman burial chamber. Obviously, they could not demolish the Roman remains for the relief road. They built an archaeological museum on the burial site and a fantastic mushroom bridge towering over the surrounding areas (some three hundred feet above the street level) had also been built. The site is a major tourist attraction now.

Figure 2.22   The Mushroom Tower in Seville

Seville is a place bristling with numerous historical and cultural monuments from both Islam and Christianity. The next morning, we were taken by a bus to have a whirlwind tour of the city - so that afterwards we could go and see individual attractions at our leisure. We saw Seville Cathedral with the Giralda, the Alcazar palace, the bullring and then we walked through the Maria Luisa park to Plaza de Espania (half-crescent palace).

Seville Cathedral (Spanish: Catedral de Santa Maria) is a Roman Catholic cathedral. It is the third largest cathedral in the world (after St Peter's cathedral in Rome and St Paul's cathedral in London). Seville was conquered by the Umayyad in 712 AD. The Almohad caliph Abu Yaqub Yusuf decided to construct a grand mosque in the city in 1172 on the site where a mosque was built in 829 by Umar Ibn Adabbas. The grand mosque that was built was massive in size (15,000 square metres internal area), but it was not completed until 1198.

Shortly after the conquest of the city by Ferdinand III, the grand mosque was 'Christianised' by converting it to the city's cathedral. In 1401, the city's leaders decided to build a massive cathedral on the site so grand that people would say after its completion that the leaders were simply mad. The work was not, however, completed until 1506!

But some aspects of the grand mosque were preserved. The courtyard for ablution for the Muslim faithful was preserved. Now it is a long pool of water, some 15 ft wide, with fountains on both sides criss-crossing the pool and orange trees adorning it. Also, the minaret of the mosque (some 342 ft high) was kept, but converted into a bell tower, known as La Giralda, which is now the iconic symbol of the city. There are wide ramps, not steps, that lead up to the bell tower. The muezzin used to go up the ramps on horseback to the bell tower to carry out calls for prayers five times a day. The cathedral also contains Christopher Columbus's burial site.

Alcazar is a royal palace, built for the Christian king, Peter of Castile, on the site of an Abbadid Muslim residential fortress. The name Alcazar comes from the Arabic word al-qasr (the castle). The castle, with its extensive garden, was used as a royal palace by the Moorish rulers. It is still being used as a royal palace and, in fact, it is the oldest royal palace in Europe. In 1987, the cathedral and the adjacent Alcazar palace complex were all given the status of World Heritage Sites.

In the evening, at 9pm, we went to the Flamenco performance. The gypsies from southern Spain created the flamenco dance and music following their arrival at Andalusia in the 15th century. It is said that the gypsies came from a region of northern India called Sid, which is now in Pakistan. The folklore of Andalusia is conveyed by vibrant expressive dance, tapping of feet and the accompanying music. It was very entertaining.

Figure 2.23   Flamenco performance

After spending three nights in Seville, we headed for the famous Moorish city of Cordoba. We did not spend the night in Cordoba, but spent the whole day there. We visited the Royal Palace, the famous Mezquita (mosque) and a museum. Cordoba, during the Moorish time, had the largest library in the world and

177

Cordoba University is reputed to be the oldest university (older than Oxford by centuries). After lunch we headed for Granada through the countryside covered with olive groves and absorbed the spectacular views of the Sierra Nevada Mountains.

We stayed in a hotel in Granada right on top of a mountain next to the Alhambra palace. Next morning, we walked to the Alhambra Palace and spent literally the whole day exploring various avenues and absorbing the lifestyles and traditions of bygone days. The history and traditions of Muslim rulers were explained to us by a local tourist guide. The tradition that the ruler would come in to one of the chambers (which chamber would not be disclosed previously for security reasons), and sit on a high chair to give audience to the public, is still being practiced by many Muslim leaders in many countries. (It is said that Sheikh Mujibur Rahman of Bangladesh practiced the same tradition). The following morning, we went on a train tour (actually a bus shaped like a train) of the city, had lunch there and came back in time to board a bus to go back to Malaga airport.

The Gulf of Mexico – a haven of tranquillity

Planning to have a cruise in the Gulf of Mexico in September/October time, invariably the hurricane season in that part of the world, is a risky undertaking. This is because the Gulf Stream - the warm ocean current – which originates on the northern edges of the equator, moves through the Caribbean Sea and then forks off to the Gulf of Mexico and the other part to the Atlantic Ocean and when the stream meets the northern cold stream, it creates a vortex of hot and humid air in the atmosphere and hence a cyclone. Recently, hurricane Dorian utterly devasted the Bahamas. But that did not deter us, as we applied our statistical insight that lightning is unlikely to strike twice at the same place!

We set off from Galveston, a dedicated port some 30 km south of Houston, Texas, in a Royal Caribbean cruise ship named Liberty of the Seas on Sunday. Our cruise ship was what is known as super-cruise ship – nearly 340 metres long, had five dining facilities, numerous restaurants and shops, a large auditorium, a running track, three swimming pools and many more facilities in 15 decks carrying nearly 3800 guests and over 1,200 staff. It took the whole morning for the guests to board on the ship and at 16:00 we set sail.

Figure 2.24   Our cruise ship, Liberty of the Seas, when docked at
Falmouth, Jamaica

There was no fanfare, no gunfire; the massive ship just quietly and smoothly slipped away from the port. As we were chatting and admiring our staterooms, I noticed that the buildings on the shore were gradually going further and further away and then started to disappear completely. Getting to know the various facilities, particularly the dining facilities – which one is for breakfast, which one for supper etc., – is quite an adventure. On top of that, my friends had to learn the naval terms like port side (left) and starboard side (right) as well as aft (back) and forward (front). I had a head start on my friends as I was a Civil Servant at the Royal Navy for a number of years.

We kept cruising along the western part of the Gulf of Mexico for nearly 40 hours until 07:00 on Tuesday morning, when the ship docked at the international pier at Cozumel, Mexico's largest island off the eastern coast of the Yucatan Peninsula. As the ship was scheduled to stay there until 16:30 in the afternoon, we were given a number of options for shore excursions. The one I chose was a trip to see the Mayan ruins in the Yucatan Peninsula, which entailed a ferry trip of 12 miles to Tulum from the ship. We had to come back by 16:30 when the ship would sail again.

Mayan civilisation is one of the oldest, if not the oldest, civilisations in the chronicle of civilisations of the world. It flourished from around 2000 *BCE* in the central American area covering the Yucatan peninsula of parts of Mexico, Belize and Guatemala, also regions of El Salvador, Columbia and Venezuela. Mayan civilisation progressed from pure agricultural living to sophisticated communal living in towns and cities. Around 600 BCE they developed logo-syllabic writing script, astronomy, sculpture, art and mathematics. In the western world, they were the first to have developed the concept of zero (rivalling India). Their counting system was based on fours, not tens (the modern-day computing algorithm is based on the binary system). However, there is an enigma about Mayan civilisation – the early Mayan civilisation lasted over two thousand years and then disappeared – for example, cities they developed were abandoned and their agriculture vanished.

Figure 2.25   Mayan Ruins in the Yucatan Peninsula

Then from 250 CE to 900 CE, the civilisation surfaced again. After 900 CE it just collapsed. Subsequently, the Mayan people were literally massacred and annihilated by the invading Spaniards in the 16th century.

Tuesday night was the captain's night. Although the captain could not be present in all three dining facilities that normally take place simultaneously, his representatives were present in all dining facilities. But more importantly, after dinner, at about 21:30 there was convivial music and dance, performed by the catering staff and any guest who felt brave enough could join in.

At 16:30 the ship sailed again from Cozumel heading eastward and reached Grand Cayman and docked at George Town the following morning (Wednesday) at 10:00. We hired a minibus to take us to the tourist spots. Although the Caribbean islands won independence in the 1970s from Britain, British influence was very much in evidence – they drive on the left side of the road. We saw the Governor's house (probably unoccupied), reminiscent of the Governor's house in the then East Pakistan. The highlight of this visit was a trip to a village called Hell. People are welcome to Hell. If our so-called religious hell is anything like this Hell, people would be grateful to be allocated to this place by our non-existent creator!

Figure 2.26   Mayan logo-syllabic writing and numbering system

At 18:00 we left George Town and set sail for Jamaica and docked at Falmouth, which is on the northern side of the island, at 08:00 on Thursday. Jamaica may be renowned for sprinters (Usain Bolt, the fastest man on earth), the fastest cricket bowler, the best basket-ball players etc., but what we saw in Falmouth was the artistic side of Jamaica. The whole precinct was full of artists painting, wood carving, engraving etc., and there were art galleries and florists etc. We had the whole day to soak up the Jamaican life in general. There were no restaurants or cafes for the obvious reason that people can pop into the ship and have a gorgeous meal at no cost and come back again to the precinct. However, coconuts and some mangoes (not very sweet) are too good to miss.

At 17:00 we got into our boat for the last leg of our journey back to Galveston. But then we had nearly 40 hours of uninterrupted cruise through the eastern side of the Gulf of Mexico. This was the opportunity to laze around, indulge in excessive eating and breathe the freshest air one can get. The catering staff were always very keen to please us.

Altogether, our Gulf of Mexico cruise was very relaxing and enjoyable. Cruising is becoming a choice holiday event for the public these days away from the hustle and bustle of big cities and towns. On top of that, because of tough competition, cruise standards are improving, and prices are very competitive.

Where land and sea mingle

We are used to visualising sea at the end of a land or land at the end of a sea, but this stereotypical image gets knocked on its head when one goes to the western outskirts of Scotland called the Hebrides. The Hebrides – both Inner and Outer – on the western fringes of Scotland offer the spectacle of land, lochs, sea and islands embracing and interlocking each other in a spectacularly serene cohabiting landscape.

The start of a sea in the Hebrides does not preclude any further land, as just a few miles of sea will usher in an island and then a few miles of the island will lead to another stretch of sea or a loch or a lochan (a small loch) and the pattern repeats a few more times. Land and sea truly intertwine there. It is estimated that there are over 31,000 lochs and lochans in Scotland alone. Loch is a Gaelic word for lake.

We started our journey by road from a bus station just outside Queen Street Railway Station in Glasgow heading towards Oban on the west coast of Scotland. We trekked along Loch Lomond and skirted around a few other lochs on our journey and, needless to say, the landscape was spectacular. On the way we stopped at Inveraray (the ancestral home of Duke of Argyll) for lunch and then proceeded towards Oban. Oban is the major ferry port connecting almost all the outlying islands in the Hebrides.

From Oban we took a ferry to go to Craignure, a ferry port, on the Isle of Mull. Mull is the second largest island (area=875 sq.km and about 45km long) in the Inner Hebrides with a population of just over 2,500 people. The island had seen better days a couple of centuries ago when the population was over 7,000 and there were trade links with Ireland and other Outer Hebrides islands. The Vikings were regular visitors to these shores, plundering the island. The Norse influence in local language, culture etc is clearly evident even now. Our hotel was situated at the edge overlooking the wider stretch of the sea. Just a short distance away from our hotel is the water stretch that is called the Sound of Mull. The name 'Sound of Mull' comes from the fact that in the olden days people from Mull used to shout out a message or call for a ferry across the narrow stretch of water from the mainland and the mainland people used to say they received the Sound of Mull.

The following day we travelled by coach through the spectacularly scenic road (mostly single tracks with *passing places*) in the Ross of Mull to Fionnphort to take a ferry to Iona. The name Iona in Gaelic means 'sacred isle'. It is truly a place where serenity merged with numinosity overwhelmed people. The most famous landmark in the island is the Iona Abbey, which was established by St. Columba in 537 CE (even before Islam was proclaimed in the deserts!). John Smith, the Labour politician and the leader of the party who could have been the British prime minister if he had lived a few more years, when he died of a heart attack in 1994, is buried just outside the Abbey. When I asked why his grave is out in the open, whereas quite a few graves are sheltered inside the Abbey, I was told that only 'noble people' are buried inside the Abbey. The Scottish feudal system is very much alive and kicking out there. We were also told that special permission was required for John Smith to be buried on the island. Next to the Abbey is the nunnery where more than 100 nuns used to live at any one time (until 19th century) and devoted their entire lives in the service of God.

Figure 2.27   *John Smith's tombstone*

After spending the whole day mulling over the relics left behind by those who served God to the best of their abilities, we left the isle of Iona by crossing the Sound of Iona to come back to Mull and then to our hotel. Whereas the Isle of Mull was one of the major trade posts for the Vikings, the isle of Iona was distinctly a devotional place.

The following day, we set off in the northerly direction through single track roads to come to Tobermory, the capital of the island. This capital is not a hustling and bustling city, but a sleepy little village of about 700 people. There is one main road by the sea having about 10 or 12 shops and, of course, a distillery producing Scottish whiskey. They are extremely proud that their whiskey is exported to as far a place as Japan!

At about 10:30 we took a ferry to go to a small island called Staffa. After about one hour of a boat trip, we reached the point where a ferry could dock. Staffa is a volcanic island with basalt columns and natural caves. The famous caves are 'Mackinnon's Cave' and 'Fingal's Cave'. Staffa is also a national nature reserve where birds have sanctuary to breed in peace. Round the edges of the columns, there are perilous wooden steps to go up to the top to see birds in their natural habitat. But this climb is not for the faint-hearted.

Figure 2.28   Mackinnon's Cave and Fingal's Cave in Staffa

After spending a couple of hours there, we set off for another, even smaller island called Lunga, which is in the range of the Treshnish Isles. This island, as well as Staffa, is uninhabited and hence it is an ideal place for a bird sanctuary. Puffins are there in large numbers at the top of the island hatching their eggs. Our guide told us that in about two months' time, parent puffins will fly off to warmer islands in the south, leaving the chicks to fend for themselves and then they themselves will fly off to the south.

After spending a couple of hours at the isle of Lunga disturbing and annoying the puffin chicks, we returned to our hotel. We spend another day at the hotel exploring the Isle of Mull at our own leisure. The following day we packed our bags in the hotel to head off to Oban and thence to Glasgow.

190

Glossary of Terms

Apartheid   Apartheid (in South African English meaning segregation or separation) was an institutionalised racial segregation that existed in South Africa from 1948 until the early 1990s when this policy was withdrawn. Apartheid was characterised by a political system that enforced racial segregation of Black, Coloured and Asian South Africans in society, politics, education, employment and housing from the Whites for the benefit of minority White population.

BCE   Before the Common Era. BCE replaces the previously used term Before Christ (BC).

CE   Common Era. This is the same as Anno Domini (AD) but without the religious connotation.

COVID-19   COVID-19 is a particular strain of coronavirus, which may have originated or first identified in the Wuhan province of China in 2019. It may have evolved or emerged in the wholesale fish market in Wuhan, but there is no confirmed evidence. It mainly affects the respiratory tract and lungs. The fatality rate is around 1 to 2 per cent in otherwise healthy persons. But the rate may be as high as 10 per cent or even more when patients have underlying health problems such as diabetes, heart problems, asthma, obesity, high blood pressure, kidney problems, COPD (Chronic Obstructive Pulmonary Disease – a collection of lung conditions) etc.

DNA   Deoxyribonucleic Acid is a molecule comprising two long chains of polynuclides coiling around each other to form a double helix with adenine, thymine, guanine and cytosine. DNA carries the genetic instructions for human lives.

GM   Genetically Modified.

Passing Place   This is a designated area for a vehicle to pull in so that the incoming vehicle can pass in a narrow single-track road in the island.

RNA   Ribonucleic Acid

Two Nation Theory (TNT)   The Two Nation Theory (TNT) asserted that Hindus and Muslims in India do not belong to one nation but two separate nations with their separate customs, tradition, education, economic conditions and religion. This theory was advanced by Allama Iqbal in 1930 and then it was adopted by the All India Muslim League conference in Lahore in 1940 and Mohammad Ali Jinnah adopted it as the founding principle of the Pakistan Movement.

UNESCO   United Nations Educational, Scientific and Cultural Organisation.

Virus   A virus is a submicroscopic infectious agent that can multiply only inside the living cells of an organism (like animals, plants or bacteria). The host cell is forced to rapidly produce large numbers of identical copies of the original virus. Unlike most living species, viruses do not have cells that can divide; new viruses can only assemble in the infected host cell. But unlike simpler infectious agents like prions, the viruses contain genes, which allow them to mutate and evolve. The genes are made of either DNA or RNA. All viruses are covered with a protein coat. More than 4,800 species of viruses have been identified. Some viruses may have evolved from plasmids – pieces of DNA that can move between cells - while others may have evolved from bacteria.

ON RELIGION

Science and Islam

Figure 3.1   *Muhammad ibn Musa al-Khwarizmi, considered to be the inventor of Algebra (780 – 850)*

The title of this write-up may seem a little unseemly as common perception dictates that science and religion are essentially two different, incompatible branches of knowledge in two different spheres of human consciousness. That may be true, but there was a time, some centuries ago, when the religion of Islam and science were good bedfellows ushering in what is now graciously called the 'Golden Age' of Islam. Sometimes this Golden Age is flashed around to brag about the illustrious ancestry of Islam and implicitly laying claim that Islam can achieve, if really determined, the same greatness in this modern world again. At other times, diehard Islamists insist that to achieve greatness one has to establish the conditions that helped achieve greatness and hence they hark back to 7th century conditions including the establishment of *Sharia laws*.

So, what is this '*Golden Age*'? The Golden Age of Islam is the period from the beginning of the 8th century to the middle of the 13th century when science and technology, art and culture, physics and philosophy, agriculture and medicine and many other disciplines flourished under the patronage of the State. The Arab kingdom, under the *Umayyad Caliphate* from 661 CE to 750 CE having Damascus as the capital and then the *Abbasid Caliphate* from 751 CE to 1258 CE having Baghdad as the capital, was the melting pot for all human knowledge. The reason for an epoch with such a rise in human culture and knowledge within just a few decades of the establishment of Islam was that the kingdom that encompassed Persia in the east to Lebanon in the west, and Egypt and North Africa in the south to the steppe of Asia Minor on the north, brought together talents from all corners of the kingdom and beyond. Greek science and technology, arts and literature were all translated into Arabic and *ilm* or knowledge was actively encouraged by the State. All the great minds of the kingdom were given the accumulated knowledge – translated from Greek, Latin and so forth – and were encouraged to pursue knowledge unencumbered by theological constraints. *"Go even unto China to seek knowledge"* was the great guiding philosophy of that period.

Tremendous progress was made in many scientific fields and many new disciplines were invented. Algebra was invented by Muhammad al-Khwarizmi (780 – 850 CE) – a *Khorasani* working in Baghdad, who not only introduced the Indian decimal concept and numeral system but also put forward logical thinking in a form which came to be known as algorithm. This algorithm is used even today as the starting point for computer

196

programming. Another *Khorasani*, Muhammad al-Farabi (872 – 950 CE) was the most prominent scientist and philosopher of the day and wrote on physics, cosmology, psychology, philosophy and much more. Yet another Khorasani scholar, Abu Rayhan al-Biruni (973 – 1048 CE), was regarded as one of the greatest scholars of the medieval Islamic era and was well versed in physics, mathematics and other natural sciences. He was a prolific scientific writer and wrote 146 treatises. His major accomplishment was that he calculated the circumference of the Earth using his trigonometric methods and that calculation came to just within 200 miles of the actual circumference of 24,900 miles! He was a great linguist too – he could converse in Persian, Arabic and Sanskrit, and knew Greek, Hebrew and Syriac. Muhammad Zakariya al-Razi (854 – 925 CE) of Persia was the pioneer in medical sciences who invented the distillation of alcohol and its use in medicine, identified measles and smallpox and wrote a treatise on them which remained the guiding light for centuries. He was the author of an encyclopaedia of medicine spanning over twenty-three volumes. Abu al-Husayn ibn-Sina was a philosopher and the most authoritative physician of the day (980 -1037 CE) and produced a multi-volume medical survey which was translated into Latin. There were many more physicists, mathematicians, astronomers and medical professionals who contributed to the great achievements of that 'Golden Age'.

Now, how did that great assimilation of knowledge in the Golden Age disappear almost overnight following the collapse of the *Abbasid Caliphate* as a result of the Mongol invasion in 1258? Can an empire as well as human achievement and intellect disappear overnight? Admittedly, other civilisations of the past such as the Ancient Greek civilisation, Indian civilisation, Chinese civilisation etc., all came and went, but none disappeared without a trace of intellectual heritage for future generations to follow as in the case of the Islamic *'Golden Age'*.

To seek out the answer, one has to look back at what was happening during the dying days of the Abbasid Caliphate. Like any great empire in decline, the Abbasid Caliphate was disintegrating for quite some time. In Spain, Christians reconquered Cordoba in 1236 and then Seville in 1248. But the last nail in the coffin was the siege and occupation of Baghdad by the Mongols in 1258, thereby bringing an end to the dying empire. For decades or even a century or more, there was internal tension and conflict between the *Mu'tazilites* who embraced rational thinking and inquisitiveness and the *Ash'arités* who were anti-rationalists. This Ash'arités movement was the dogmatic Sunni Muslim movement which held the dogma that the rationalist view was anti-Islamic. Things happen as God wishes them to happen, not as a priori or a posteriori.

Abu Hamid al-Ghazali (1058–1111 CE) argued that rationalism was incompatible with Islamic teaching. As God's will is completely free and unencumbered, His wishes are supreme and could not be compromised by the rationalisation of causes and effects. A storm takes place because God wishes it that way to punish the affected people for their sins, not as a result of meteorological condition. Rain falls not as a result of precipitation and condensation of cloud, but by sheer God's will. By his dogmatic interpretation of Islam, he gave a philosophical underpinning of religion and brought Sunni Islam very close to Sufi philosophy.

Following the collapse of the Abbasid Caliphate, the Ash'arités movement supported by the *Ghazalites* took hold in the Islamic world. From that time on, Islam had been going in the opposite direction to their erstwhile rationalist philosophy and that which Western Christianity readily adopted. Admittedly, Christianity had its turbulent periods when different theological strands vied against each other and did everything to eliminate each other, but eventually rationality prevailed over darkness. Christianity came out of the Dark Ages bruised and battered, but with its theology, intermingled with rationality, prevailing.

The Western World embraced the *Renaissance* (Age of Reason) and the *Age of Enlightenment* and separated theology from the functioning of the State. In other words, a clear demarcation was laid between the theology and its boundary of influence and the workings of the nation State and its sphere of influence.

Islam does not want to accept such segregation of duties and responsibilities. It wants to encroach on the State responsibilities covering politics, economics, education and every other field of human endeavour. How could a State function when religion tells that there is no rationality, no cause and effect; everything moves as God desires? How could a State develop economically or intellectually when religion puts a stopper over its advancement? One simple event will expose this disconnect.

Some years ago, when I went from Britain to Saudi Arabia as a Consultant on Radiological Protection, I was invited to present a paper on the 'Effects of radiation on human beings' at an international seminar in Riyadh. The seminar was very well attended with many British, American, German, Swedish and Finnish experts. There was a high-level Saudi presence too, including the Saudi Interior Minister, Health Minister and Saudi Atomic Energy Commission's chairman and so forth. As I presented my paper in English, it had to be translated into Arabic as I spoke. During the presentation, I said that there was a contemporary scientific view that radiation might have caused a mutation in human genes that helped the process of evolution. My translator, a clever Egyptian man, stopped translating at that point and then came over to me to say, "Sir, I cannot translate this line. If I do, not only I but you would also be arrested for heresy." Then it dawned on me that this is a fundamentalist country where there is no evolution, God made everything. We proceeded without this sentence and any other reference to *Darwinism*. Science was relegated to the dictates of religion.

In most of the fundamentalist Muslim countries, education at schools, colleges and universities proceeds without any reference to evolution and natural selection. Islamic teaching takes precedence over scientific developments – God created the Earth, Sun, Moon and everything else some 10,000 years ago; everything happens as God desires; human beings must pray to God to please Him, and He will give things as He pleases! With such blockheaded theology, it is no wonder that science and technology have disappeared from the Islamic world.

Physics Nobel Laureate Steven Weinberg (who shared the prize with *Abdus Salam* and Sheldon Glashow in 1979) said, *"Though there are talented scientists of Muslim origin working productively in the West, for forty years I have not seen a single paper by a physicist or an astronomer working in a Muslim country that was worth reading."*

Religion and Morality

Religious scholars and even some philosophers lay claims that religion and morality are intricately intertwined; without morality religion would be baseless and without religion morality would be without foundation. The main purpose of religion is to impart moral values to mankind. When religion instils morality, humanity sees the true value of life, the unbridled beauty of life and the majestic creation; without morality humans would lead a life in depravity.

All these high-sounding, lofty preaching of the religious scholars may appear to have deep inner meaning; but one must appreciate that religion has no unique claim on morality. In fact, most of the religions embody in practice just the reverse – sectarian, antagonistic and insular codes for the followers of a particular religion. These basic traits of a religion are against the very grains of morality. To appreciate the inner discord between religion and morality, let us look at the meaning and essence of morality.

Morality fundamentally embodies the 'corporate rule' – the rule embracing cooperation among the people of the community, society, the country and beyond. The corporate rule that brings benefits to all in a cooperative way - for all, not for just the few – is a moral imperative. In the terminology of the game theory, it can be stated that morality inherently offers more than zero sum. If an attribute brings benefit to some people at the cost of others, then that attribute may be called zero sum issue and that has no moral underpinning. For example, when a government taxes the rich to help the poor, that may be considered a good political decision, but not a moral issue. On the other hand, if an attribute brings benefit to everybody, equally or proportionately, without harming any particular section, that can be viewed as a moral decision. For example, giving free education to all within a country or free medical care at the point of need may be considered a moral undertaking. Morality brings benefit to

201

everybody and hence it is viewed as offering more than zero sum.

Morality maybe considered to have seven basic strands, these are: *Family, Group, Reciprocity, Heroism, Deference, Fairness* and *Property*. Human beings, being social animals, tend to live together in the family and the inherent desire of fair, equitable and cooperative distribution of benefits drawn collectively among the small bubble of family members constitutes the first strand of morality. The morality of the *Group* is an extension of that of the *Family* issue. What can be shared and sacrificed within the wider circle of the group, beyond the family, is the Group morality. The morality of *Reciprocity* is that if one person helps another person at the time of need, it is a moral imperative on the recipient to reciprocate the initial help at the right occasion. It helps both the initial giver and the recipient when it is needed most. *Heroism* is that strand of morality when one carries out a task to help others even at risk to himself. The morality of Heroism is not to earn the plaudit of heroism, but an impartial attempt to help others. An example of it can be given, as recently when a Chinese man fell into a river in Shanghai and was struggling to save his life, a British diplomat (aged well over 60) instinctively jumped into the river and pulled the man to the shore and saved his life. This is the morality of Heroism - without any expectation for any reward or plaudit – a pure desire to help others in need. *Deference* implies submission or yielding to the judgement of recognised superiors or higher officials and thereby maintaining harmonious relationships in society. This is an important part of morality by maintaining corporate culture. *Fairness* comes as an essential element of morality as without it the whole corporate rule would break down to chaos. What is right, what is true, what is wrong etc., should be established with Fairness as part of morality. And finally, *Property* offers the morality of maintaining one's right to own and maintain property and possession. As a proverb goes, an Englishman's home is his castle. It is morally right that he should be allowed to live in his own home in a safe and dignified way and that is part of morality.

All of these strands, singly or collectively, offer the spirit and essence of morality. Morality is not only ethically justifiable but is also beneficial from an evolutionary point of view. Individual genes of an organic body may exhibit selfish behaviour, but when it comes to the welfare of the survival machine (the whole body), morality encompassing corporate rule plays a dominant role. A moral society encourages a code of conduct where all people may live comfortably, equitably and in dignified ways.

Now the big question is, what role does religion play in maintaining morality or corporate rule? To answer this question, one has to trace back what role religion plays traditionally. The basic premise is that a religion inherently wants to establish its superiority and supremacy over other religions - as religions are competing against one another. This very basic competitive strand goes against the grain of the morality of corporate rule. One religion does not accept or tolerate another religion's theological stand and that is evident by their mutual antagonism and centuries of fighting. So, there cannot be a universal morality applicable to the whole society comprising various religions. The morality of cooperation, reciprocity, fairness, property etc., may be applicable to people within a particular religion, but they may not be extended to people of other religions.

So, a theocratic state having people of many religious affiliations cannot get a morally justifiable rule. Morality becomes subservient to theocracy or may even be abandoned in favour of theocratic dogma, as in many Islamic states and even in India at the moment. The claims by the religious scholars and leaders that religion is the custodian of morality and that without religion morality would disappear, are absurdly ludicrous and without any basis. Religion is detrimental to morality, as religion is sectarian whereas morality requires corporate rule. Therefore, one can say religion is amoral, not immoral.

203

Almost all philosophers, psychologists, evolutionary biologists, writers, thinkers, scientists and so forth have expressed views that morality is not a good bedfellow to religion, in fact just the opposite. Their dislike to associate religion with morality had been expressed in many different ways and one particular area where their abhorrence was expressed firmly against religions was when assessed against the perceived punishment and reward as depicted in religious books.

The British philosopher and polymath, **Bertrand Russell**, Nobel Laureate in literature in 1950, expressed his revulsion against religion when he said, "*Religion is based mainly upon fear, fear of the mysterious, fear of defeat, fear of death. Fear is the parent of cruelty, and therefore it is no wonder if cruelty and religion have gone hand in hand.*"

Albert Einstein, Nobel Laureate in Physics in 1921, said, "*If people are good only because they fear punishment, and hope for reward, then we are a sorry lot indeed.*"

Christopher Hitchens, a British intellectual, said, "*Human decency is not derived from religion; it precedes it.*"

Thus, religion and morality do not go hand in hand in the modern society. The secularism within the Constitution may provide the rightful place for morality, overriding the communalism and sectarianism of various religions.

Why are Muslims regressive?

It may be somewhat disingenuous to compartmentalise *monotheistic religions* (also known as Abrahamic religions) into separate boxes in order to assess an individual religion's successes and failures, but this is exactly what this article aims to do, notwithstanding the sentimental or emotional attachments of ardent adherents. In this pursuit, Islam is going to be scrutinised closely to decipher its achievements vis-à-vis other monotheistic religions. The purpose is definitely not to denigrate or even undermine any religion, but to seek out the root causes for differences in achievements.

Among the three monotheistic religions, Christianity with all its sects and denominations is the largest religious group. Nearly 30 per cent of the world population of around 7.5 billion people (over 2.2 billion) is Christian. They are also most successful in science and technology, art and literature and in almost all other human intellectual pursuits. But this success does not derive from their numerical superiority but by their intrinsic ability to adapt, adopt and assimilate views and ideas from other cultures and societies.

Christianity did, however, go through the internecine religious conflicts over the centuries but those were in the Dark Ages (5th to 10th centuries). Those conflicts were not only between the various factions or denominations of the Christian religion but also between the religions and the States. The dawn of the *'Age of Enlightenment'* led to some sort of tacit accommodation between the States and the religions whereby the States were assigned the responsibilities for political, social, economic, military etc. matters and religion became the guardian and flag bearer of the moral and ethical standards of the people. Religion with divine edicts became the institution of moral values and not the gatekeeper of all human things, nor was it the 'be all and end all' of human conscience. In other words, some sort of secularity was inbuilt in the Christian conscience.

Figure 3.2   The Age of Enlightenment – 17th to 19th centuries

This separation of duties between the State and religion released unbridled human energy from destructive pursuits to constructive regeneration. Scientific research and development, exploration of unknown things, the Industrial Revolution, modern art and literature, are all due to human endeavour devoted to the improvement of human conditions and knowledge without the distraction of religious infighting.

Leaving Christianity aside, one can say that Islam and Judaism are more or less on the same platform – adherents of both of these religions are extremely devotional and many of them are emotionally attached. So, a valid comparison between these two religions may lead to some meaningful insight.

Both of these religions originated roughly in the same geographical area — *Makkah* and *Canaan* in the Middle East – although not at the same time. Needless to say, Judaism is the precursor to Islam and many of the rituals from Judaism have been assimilated in Islam, either literally or with some edifications. The Jewish prophets – Abraham, Isaac, Jacob, Moses and so forth are also the prophets of Islam. The commonality between Islam and Judaism is unmistakable.

Despite these ancestral links or, one can say the umbilical cord, these two religions have long been at loggerheads with each other right from the beginning and have divergent outlooks. In political, social, economic and technical fields, as well as in arts and literature or any other field of human endeavour, Jews have been by far more successful than the Muslims. How did this wide disparity in achievement between these two religious adherents come about in the present-day world? This disparity becomes even starker when the population of Muslims and Jews of the present-day world are taken into account.

Figure 3.3   *Reading the Quran, the Islamic holy book, in Bangladesh.*

There are over 1,650 million Muslims in the world today as against only about 16 million Jews. Thus, for every single Jew in the world, there are nearly 100 Muslims. Whereas in 54 sovereign States in the world, Muslims are in majority and run those States, there is only one State — Israel — where Jews are in the majority and run that State. There are countries such as Saudi Arabia, Afghanistan, Iran and so forth where nearly 99 per cent of the population are Muslims. Even in some non-Muslim countries there are large Muslim population. There are about 7 million Jews in Israel and over 8 million in North and South America. There are some 1,000,000 or so Jews scattered around European countries and in other countries such as Egypt, Syria and Lebanon.

One measure of achievement of these two religious groups can be gauged by the number of Nobel Prizes received by them. The Nobel Prizes, the most prestigious awards in the world for intellectual achievements, have been awarded in Physics, Chemistry, Physiology or Medicine, Literature and Peace Studies since 1901 and in Economics since 1969. The Jews received more than 22 per cent of all Nobel prizes, although they constitute just over 0.2 per cent of the world population. Altogether Jews received 184 Nobel prizes (including 8 in Peace Studies) until 2020, while carrying out research works in various countries, sometimes under hostile environments. On the other hand, Muslims received only 12 Nobel prizes (including 7 in Peace Studies) until 2020, while making up over 21 per cent of the world population. It may be stated that the peace prizes are awarded primarily on socio-political grounds which have impacts on society, not so much on intellectual prowess. If Peace Studies are excluded from the tally of prizes, Jews have hauled 176 prizes whereas Muslims have received only 5 prizes. (It may be pointed out that Prof. *Abdus Salam* from Pakistan, who won the Nobel Prize in Physics in 1979, was declared by the Pakistani authorities to be a non-Muslim as he belonged to the Ahmadiyya sect, which was declared non-Muslim.) Thus, the Jews are more than 35 times more successful in winning Nobel prizes (excluding peace prizes) than the Muslims, although constituting only one hundredth of the Muslim population!

Figure 3.4   A Madrassah class

But this sheer number of Nobel prizes does not do full justice to the contributions of the Jews to the world of science. Albert Einstein, the most celebrated and influential scientist, was a Jew. Other most renowned Jewish physicists were Wolfgang Pauli (Pauli Exclusion Principle), Niels Bohr (Bohr Atomic Model), Max Born (Quantum Theorist), Richard Feynman (Quantum Mechanics) – all of them made monumental contributions to modern physics. Sigmund Freud, Karl Marx and Milton Friedman were also Jews. The contributions the Jews have made in the fields of literature, arts and culture are also truly astounding.

The reason why Jews are highly successful may be that they have high respect for knowledge and that they have a single-minded approach to success. Moreover, there is a very large section of Jews who are open-minded, rational and pragmatic.

During the 18th, 19th and 20th centuries, Jews were dispersed throughout the whole of Europe as they had no homeland of their own and their survival in society depended on their success. During the early part of the 20th century, the Jews excelled in science and literature in Germany, Austria, the Czech Republic, Italy, the UK and so forth.

Almost all the reputable German academic institutions were headed by Jews (mostly Ashkenazi) in the 1920s and 1930s; all major medical establishments were under Jewish control and arts and literature were dominated by Jews. Their domination was so complete that Hitler realised that German supremacy and Aryan culture could not be revived without getting rid of Jews. He used to view Jews as leeches, which suck out lifeblood from the host body. The Nazi regime started deporting and exterminating Jews. Göttingen University, the cradle of quantum mechanics, was completely dominated by Jewish physicists and mathematicians. The Nazi Minister for Education asked David Hilbert, a highly respected and prominent non-Jewish mathematician in charge of the University, whether it was true that the Institute suffered from the departure of Jews and their friends. *"Suffered? No, Herr Minister, it did not suffer. It just does not exist anymore,"* replied Professor Hilbert.

As against such excellence among the Jews in the 19th and 20th centuries (as well as in the 21st century), the Muslims throughout the world had moved in the opposite direction. Instead of striving for excellence in human endeavour, they shunned Western science, education, literature and culture. In the Indian Subcontinent in the 19th century, Muslims, as a show of defiance to the British Raj, took the conscious decision to boycott Western education and adopted religious education instead. It was only during the beginning of the 20th century that Muslims realised that without education they could not rid themselves of the colonial yoke and they accepted Western education reluctantly.

Many of the Muslim theologians of today, taking cue from the past when Islam was at the forefront of science and civilization, advocate going back to the roots and adopting religion wholeheartedly. Hardly do they realise that when Islam was at the forefront during the 9th to 13th centuries, they adopted science and technology, and the arts and literature of the day wholeheartedly and pursued them vigorously; they did not seek out scientific knowledge from the holy book of Quran and Hadith. Due to the lapse of attention during the fading years of Islamic glory, the mantle of science and civilization had slipped away from the Muslims to the Western world.

The other two religions (Christianity and Judaism) tacitly accepted the reality of the modern world and positioned themselves accordingly. The Chief Rabbi of the United Hebrew Congregations of the Commonwealth said recently in London that science has a religious dignity. The Archbishop of Canterbury circumvented the conflict by saying that Darwin's theory of evolution is the most enthralling of ideas worthy of embracing. But Islam steadfastly refuses to accept scientific knowledge and values.

Albert Einstein famously said, *"Learn from yesterday, live for today and hope for tomorrow. The important thing is not to stop questioning."* If free thinking and scientific inquiry are stifled in the minds of adherents of a religion, then those adherents will be ignoramuses and become automatons. The religion itself will gradually become a religion of such morons and disappear from the enlightened populace.

Does Islam need reforming?

Islam has come a long way, both in physical space and time, from the remote deserts of *Makkah* at the far-gone ages of the 7th century *CE* to becoming one of the largest religions of the world in the twenty-first century. But its development and progress had not always been smooth and amiable. It has withstood and weathered tumultuous events over the past 14 centuries or so - some periods of which were glorious and enthralling while others were vicious and shameful. Such tumultuous progress may be inherent to all the monotheistic religions, that vie against each other to attract wider human allegiance in the rough and tough world of religious numinosity; but Islam has had more than its fair share of turbulence.

Among the three *monotheistic (Abrahamic) religions,* Christianity with all its sects and denominations is the largest religion. Nearly 30 per cent of the world population of 7.5 billion people belong to Christianity - altogether over 2.2 billion. They are most successful in science and technology, astronomy and philosophy, arts and literature, and in almost all other human intellectual endeavours. This success does not come about from their numerical superiority but from their willingness and eagerness to adapt, adopt and assimilate ideas, views and knowledge on its way.

Christianity did, of course, go through the internecine religious conflicts over the centuries, but those conflicts spanning over centuries were in the long past of the Middle Ages. Those conflicts were not only confined to various sects and denominations of Christianity; they were also between the religion and the State. The dawn of the *Age of Enlightenment* led to reconciliation and some sort of tacit accommodation between the State and the Church (representing religion) - whereby the Church relinquished to the State the responsibility for political, social, economic, military and all other stately matters and the

213

State passed on proprietary roles over moral codes and numinous matters to the Church. In other words, the Church was no longer the custodian of all things of human conscience. Thus, some sort of separation of functions – the concept of secularity – was instilled in the Christian mindset.

This separation of duties between the State and religion diverted an enormous amount of energy from destructive purposes to constructive pursuits. Scientific research and development, modern art and literature, medical sciences and astronomy, sports and games were all due to human endeavour devoted to improving human knowledge and human well-being without the destructive pull of religious in-fighting.

Islam, on the other hand, got embroiled in vicious conflicts almost right from the inception. In fact, the fault line that emerged right after the demise of Prophet Mohammad has never been mended even to the present day. However, despite antagonistic stances taken up by various sects of Islam, it survived and even flourished over a certain period of time. Numerically, Islam is the second largest religion in the world today consisting of nearly 1,650 million adherents. But it has not been able to achieve successes materialistically or intellectually in the modern era as Christianity or Judaism has done. There are very good reasons – some of them intrinsic and inbuilt whereas others are purely self-inflicted.

Judaism is the oldest and the smallest of the *Abrahamic monotheistic religions*. Abraham started the religion of Judaism some 3,500 years ago based on a single, all powerful unified God. Subsequently, Christianity, some 2,000 years ago, and Islam, some 1,400 years ago, followed this thread of the unity God – a God who is omnipotent, omnipresent, omniscient and all-powerful. The progress of Judaism had turned out to be very turbulent; it was littered with events of persecution, pogrom and ethnic cleansing of Jews over the centuries. At present, there are only about 15 million Jews in Israel and America put together, and about another million scattered over Europe and various other Middle East countries.

Nearly 1,650 million Muslims are scattered over 54 sovereign Muslim States of the world. The Kingdom of Saudi Arabia is the richest of the Muslim States and the King is the custodian of the two holiest mosques - in *Makkah* and Madina - in Islam. With financial and religious powers come political power. As the dominant Islamic State, Saudi Arabia has imposed a version of Islam – the *Wahhabism / Salafism* to which it clings most assiduously. It is claimed by Saudi Arabia that Wahhabism is the puritanical version of Islam – the so-called fundamental strand of Islam – and hence must be upheld by Muslims.

The main plank of Wahhabism is the Islamic law, which is known as *Sharia Law*. Many egregious claims and laws were incorporated in Sharia law. For instance, it is claimed that Sharia law is divinely ordained and immutable: it proclaims that *blasphemers* and *apostates* should be killed; women should be confined to the boundaries of their homes; men were given out their guardianship irrespective of their ages; and that women should be covered up completely and accompanied by men whenever they go out of their homes.

These claims are gaining acceptance not only in Muslim countries of the East but also in European and American countries. In Western countries, Muslim mullahs started asserting that even the *hijab*, let alone the *burqa and niqab*, is obligatory in Islam and hence must be donned by women as well as by girls beyond the age of puberty (roughly 12 years).

All of these proclaimed divine laws and ordains, as contained in the Sharia, must be accepted in its entirety by Muslims. These laws cannot be questioned or challenged, and any violation would be regarded as sin and would be punished severely by *Allah*. But the fact is that these ordinances were invented in the 9th century, nearly two centuries after the death of Prophet Mohammad, by the *Abbasid Muslim Empire*.

215

The law of *apostasy* was introduced to discourage any revolt against the state under the Abbasid rule. The law on blasphemy was also state-sanctioned. The blasphemy law was used by the colonial powers to maintain harmony between different religious groups. But now many Muslim countries such as Saudi Arabia, Egypt, Pakistan, Iran and so forth, realising their potential administrative advantages, uplifted these sanctions to divine status and started claiming them as sacrosanct and inviolable. In Pakistan, the military dictator Zia-ul-Haq in 1982, so as to garner support from the ultra-conservative religious parties, made it a central plank of his repressive rule. As it was claimed to be divinely ordained, no human being could even question its validity. If anybody did, he was questioning the religion itself!

This practice of promulgating extremely repressive ordinances in the name of religion has been in practice for centuries in Islam. In the 10th century CE, the Abbasid Caliph Abdul Qadir even denounced 'critical thinking' and called such efforts as 'counter to Islam'. He ordered his subjects to dissociate themselves from philosophers and free thinkers, despite the fact that numerous verses in the Quran exhort believers to think and raise questions. These promulgations at some point during the *Golden Ages of Islam*, gradually became entrenched in the textbooks, which became part of the Sharia laws in later days. So, when in Bangladesh and in other Muslim countries, extremists viciously kill people whom they regard as free thinkers, such as humanists, writers, poets, philosophers etc., these violent murders are carried out in the mistaken belief of religious obligations!

Figure 3.5   Agitation by Islamists in Bangladesh

Even though the Abbasid Caliphate is regarded as the 'Golden Age of Islam', the conflict between the freethinkers and the brain-washed religious followers was not too far below the surface. Almost throughout the whole of the Abbasid Caliphate, the clash between the *Mu'tazilites* embracing rationalism and inquisitiveness and the *Ash'arités* movement embracing an anti-rationalist philosophy had been simmering right across. The Ash'arités movement was a dogmatic *Sunni Muslim* movement who held the view that the rationalists were anti-Islamic. Things happen because God wishes them to happen, not as a result of cause and effect. The rationalist Mu'tazilites had the upper hand only because they could show intellectual superiority and scientific successes and that kept Ash'arités at bay in those days. (See 'Science and Islam'). When around 1240 CE to 1260 CE the Abbasid Caliphate crumbled, the Mu'tazilites disappeared almost overnight and the *'Golden Age'* of Islam almost dissolved out of existence.

So, this clash of rationalism and dogmatic religious fundamentalism is not of present day making. It has been going on right from the very beginning, through the *'Golden Age'* and into the present age. When in the 18th century, Indian Muslims adopted the policy of 'Boycott English' in the name of nationalism, it had a religious undertone. By boycotting English education and culture in the colonial regime, Muslims had effectively harmed themselves in the mistaken belief that they were harming the colonial masters. In fact, that boycott helped the British Raj tremendously – they had to deal with one community only, as the other dominant community had relegated themselves into illiteracy and irrelevance. The damage caused by that singular decision by Muslims has not been recovered even to this day. The decline of Muslims in India and, indeed, throughout the whole of the Muslim world is so precipitous that unless there is a drastic reformation of Islamic teaching, Islam as a religion may face an existential problem. There seems to be a need to either reform Islam – review Islamic doctrines to accommodate modern scientific ideas - or relegate religion to the background such that it does not come in contact with the State and its scientific values and political functions.

Internecine conflict in Islam

The world of Islam with more than 1650 million adherents spread over almost all the continents of the world is not in a very happy state now. In fact, this religion is in a dire state. This state of affairs arises not because Islam is under attack externally from rival religions, although there is some discernible evidence supporting this notion, but mainly because it is perennially in the throes of intra-religious animosity which is now surfacing as a violent internecine conflict. This conflict is of late taking on such severe dimensions that the very foundation of the religion is in danger of being seriously shaken or even damaged.

The sectarian conflict in Islam is not of recent making. The two major sects of Islam – *Sunni* and *Shia* – have been at loggerheads right from the time of the Battle of Karbala in 680 CE. After the death of Prophet Muhammad in 632 CE, the religion faced a serious succession problem. The monolithic structure of the religion, which Prophet Muhammad had built up almost single-handedly in his own lifetime, started to crumble immediately after his death. The split did not come about on ideological differences but because of political rivalry and a power struggle between the Prophet's tribe and the heir of his family. Prophet Muhammad did not leave any sons and his only daughter was married to his first cousin, Ali, who came from a different tribe. Although the son-in-law, Ali, was Mohammad's chosen successor and should be the legitimate heir to the Islamic empire to assume the Caliphate, he was effectively out-manoeuvered by the leaders of the Quraysh tribe on the grounds that Ali did not come from the same tribe. It may be recalled that the tribe was at that time the central piece of Arab society and most seriously adhered to for physical, moral and economic protection. Hence the leaders of the tribe chose Abu Bakr, a prominent leader of the Quraysh tribe, as their first Caliph. For the sake of unity and cohesion in Islam, Ali accepted this decision as well as the

219

decisions to select next two Caliphs from the same tribe, bypassing him.

Eventually when he became the fourth Caliph of Islam, he had to face hostility from the Quraysh tribe and revolts by the followers of the previous three Caliphs. On Ali's death, after some political dissent and tribal antagonisms, his son, Husayn, was invited to take up his position as the next Caliph in Kufah in Iraq in 680 CE. But there was a sinister plot and as he was going to Kufah from Makkah with his family to take up the position, he was ambushed at Karbala by the army of the rival Caliph supported by the Quraysh tribe. He, along with his family, was slain in the Battle of Karbala in 680 CE. That battle and the massacre ensuing thereof left an indelible mark of savagery in Islamic history and it formed the watershed of a permanent split in Islam making two sects in Islam — the Sunnis, the followers of the first three Caliphs - and the Shias, followers of Ali and his descendants. That animosity and hostility between these two sects became so deeply ingrained that it remained burning and undiminished even today.

The Sunni remained the dominant sect in Islam ever since and it effectively remained the flagbearer of Islam, totally overshadowing the Shia sect. However, during the period of the 7th century to about the 13th century, when Sunnis along with Shias and other smaller denominations pursued science and literature, art and music, architecture and all other human intellectual pursuits with utmost vigour and energy, the internal differences remained subdued. The Islamic world collectively achieved unimaginable cultural successes. Those were the *Golden Ages of Islam* and it was at the forefront of human civilisation. There was hardly any discontent and discord between the sects or denominations.

Since the start of *Wahhabi ideology* by Abd-al Wahhab (from Jaid, what is now in Saudi Arabia) in the 18th century and the adoption of this ideology by Mohammad ibn-Saud, the ruler of Diriyah, Saudi Arabia, the age-old fault line between the first three Caliphs of Islam and the subsequent developments of Islam from the fourth Caliph of Islam, Ali, re-emerged. In fact, the division was exacerbated by Sunnis adopting the fundamentalist Wahhabi ideology, whereas Shias upheld the extant ideology of the day. The Wahhabi movement, which may also be branded as Salafism, is the ultra-conservative Islamic ideology which rejects any interpretation of original Islamic teachings as unacceptable and impure – branding such practices as sheer innovation and revisionist in character. This movement demands that Islam must rely exclusively on the Quran and Hadith as propounded by Prophet Mohammad and the first three Caliphs – the fundamentalist ideology. This dogma effectively excluded Shias from the mainstream of Islam, which Sunnis effectively claimed to be theirs alone.

Figure 3.6   Rivalry between Islamic sects

At the start of the alliance between Mohammad ibn-Saud and Abd-al Wahhab, it was agreed that the Wahhabi movement of Abd-al Wahhab would be enforced and promulgated throughout the Arab land (and beyond) by ibn-Saud and his heirs in return for the ibn-Saud family retaining the proprietary right of the movement. Since that time, ibn-Saud and his heirs kept their promise, and *Wahhabism* became almost synonymous with ibn-Sauds' ideology and the kingdom of Saudi Arabia became the vanguard of Wahhabism.

The Saud family clung to this fundamentalist ideology of Islam not so much out of conviction for the purity of the ideology but as a strategic planning that by adopting this fundamentalist ideology they would have the legitimacy of Islam to rule over the holy land of Saudi Arabia. The king of Saudi Arabia became the custodian of two holy mosques in Saudi Arabia and hence he was, de-facto, the keeper of Islam and Islamic ideology in all its purity and pugnaciousness as enunciated in the Quran and Hadith. This is the religious/ideological basis of ibn-Sauds' claim over the land of Saudi Arabia and the Islamic world.

During the next 140 years since the alliance, ibn-Sauds mounted various campaigns against other sects of Islam – particularly against the Shia. In 1802 they attacked the city of Karbala – the most holy city for the Shias, ransacked the city, killed thousands of civilians and destroyed the dome over the grave of al-Husayn (son of Ali). Since the late 1940s when Saudi Arabia as a country started to become affluent on the back of petrodollars, there was discernible evidence of the gradual rise of Wahhabism. The country spent over $87 billion propagating Wahhabism throughout the world over the last 60 years or so. They overtly and covertly subsidised and donated funds to almost every country in the world to set up mosques, Islamic centres, Islamic schools, madrasas and Muslim ummahs (communities).

These outlets offered Saudi Arabia the springboard to spread Wahhabism or fundamentalist Islamic ideology all over the world. It carried out its operation very discreetly and surreptitiously so that no suspicion or antagonism was aroused in the host country. Many schools, colleges, universities, big industrial organisations in many Western countries had seen the seed corn of Islamic Centres sprouting up with Saudi funds, taking advantage of the religious freedom of liberal democracies in the host countries. Radical Imams were recruited to the mosques to nurture Wahhabism. It then became a very small step from this fundamentalist religiosity to Jihadist ideology.

Figure 3.7   Portrayal of the fundamentalist Wahhabi myth

When the then USSR invaded Afghanistan in 1979 to prop up the pro-Russian regime in that country, there was a large number of ready-made Jihad ideologists in the Western countries too eager to go and fight the infidels. The Western governments, particularly the USA through the CIA, channelled large amounts of money, arms and ammunitions to the Mujahedeen comprising local and foreign Jihadists to fight the aggressors. Pakistan offered military support and intelligence through Inter-Services Intelligence (ISI) and Saudi Arabia offered financial assistance and theological backing. The USSR (present day Russia) was

223

defeated and was forced to withdraw. The CIA backed Mujahedeen, which later became the backbone of the Taliban and al-Qaeda, took over the country and established an Islamic State. They introduced Sharia Laws – banned women's education, banned modern education to introduce Islamic education through madrasas and destroyed art and culture associated with non-Islamic tradition. The country became a safe haven for terrorist organisations and Osama bin Laden was given official sanctuary there.

The success of Afghanistan to become a fundamentalist Islamic state was the springboard for further expansion of Wahhabism throughout the whole world. The hands that fed Mujahedeen/Taliban in their infancy in Afghanistan were now bitten hard and Pakistan was in mortal danger of being swallowed up by the Taliban. The tribal regions of the North-West Frontier Province of Pakistan, which were traditionally unruly and fractious, became the first areas to be taken over by the fundamentalist Taliban. At the same time, numerous religious organisations started to crop up in cities and towns in Pakistan and, needless to say, their expansion was accompanied by extreme violence. The Ahmadi sect belonging to Shia ideology was declared non-Islamic by the religious zealots in Pakistan, which was then upheld by the Pakistani religious hierarchy.

This process of backdoor *Islamisation* propagating Wahhabism had been going on ever since Bangladesh came into existence in 1971. Organisations such as ibn-Sina Bank, ibn-Sina Hospital and Medical Centre, ibn-Sina School/College, mosques, madrasas etc., were set up with Saudi Arabian money or assistance to attract people to Islamic identity (Wahhabism). There were many ingenuous ways of supporting religious activities. For example, when a Muslim planned to go to Mecca to perform Hajj, he/she had to have a medical certificate and that medical certificate could only be given by the ibn-Sina Hospital. The money accrued from this closed practice of offering

224

certificates was ploughed back into madrasas, ibn-Sina educational establishments etc. In addition, there were financial kickbacks to corrupt politicians to support Islamic ideology and activities within the country. The ideology that was spread under all these activities was nothing other than Wahhabi fundamentalism.

In Iraq, when Saddam Hussein was overthrown, the conflict between the Sunni and the Shia, which was never too far below the surface, bubbled up and engulfed the entire country and the internecine conflict started with all its ferocity. Islamist fighters calling themselves Jihadists and purporting Wahhabi ideology congregated from various parts of the world – Afghanistan, Bosnia, Chechnya, Kashmir, Saudi Arabia and Pakistan — to fight the Shias and eliminate them.

The war that raged in Syria was nothing but the intra-religious conflict between Shia and Sunni. There was the veneer of *Arab Spring* fighting the dictatorship of Bashar al-Assad to establish democratic rights, but beneath it all was the blood feud of Islam. Saudi Arabia, Qatar and other Gulf States were pouring money, arms and ammunition to rebels who were dominantly Sunni fighters and they were joined by al-Qaeda jihadists to fight against the Shias represented by the *Alawite regime* of Bashar al-Assad. This clear religious divide could be seen when Hamas (Lebanese Sunni militia) joined the rebels and Hezbollah (Lebanese Shia militia) joined the Assad regime. Turkey, a Sunni country, was supporting rebels whereas Iran, a Shia country, was supporting the Assad regime. So, Shia-Sunni religious conflict raged in all its ferocity in Syria, sucking in Western powers inadvertently.

The sectarian conflicts in the Middle East may not all have their roots firmly embedded in the Shia-Sunni divide, but the major ones are definitely so. The decade long in-fighting and bloodbath in Lebanon, the present sectarian killing in Iraq, Afghanistan, Pakistan, Libya and so forth are all rooted in Shia-Sunni conflict. In Pakistan, Sunni Muslims instigated by

225

religious zealots perpetrated bestial murders of Shias in the name of religion.

Then there is the additional religious divide: the fundamentalist Sunni upholding Wahhabism and the moderate Sunni. The conflict in Egypt between the *Muslim Brotherhood* purporting Wahhabism and the so-called secularists believing in moderate Sunni theology should be seen in that light. A similar situation is brewing up in Bangladesh almost imperceptibly. The Jamaat-e-Islam, Hifazat-e Islam and many other religious-political parties are following Wahhabi ideology almost obliviously through their ignorance.

The internecine conflicts that are raging overtly all over the Islamic world and covertly in the non-Islamic world are damaging the very foundation of Islam. When faced with the regressive positions of the Muslims vis-à-vis other religious followers, the Muslim theologians came out with the overt solution that progress could only be achieved through the enforcement of strict ideological purity and by rejecting Western modern education. The basis of such a theological dogma was mistakenly based on the presumption that Islam achieved greatness during the *'golden ages'* by adhering strictly to its religious values. Nothing could be further from the truth and it is extremely dangerous to underpin theological basis on incorrect historical presumptions.

Islam achieved greatness by following wholeheartedly science and technology, art and culture etc., and relegating religious dogma completely. If religion is rejected as the main anchor in the Islamic world today, then the historical schism that had dogged Shias and Sunnis from the beginning will lessen in strength and the religion can coexist with other religions in the modern world.

Is religion really in decline?

Figure 3.8   Religious practice of praying

A recent study by a bio-psychologist, Nigel Barber, reported in the *Huffington Post*, shows that religion is in decline worldwide and the pace of decline is likely to be faster in future such that by 2041 religion, as we know it today, will disappear completely! By religion, he meant the blind faith of total and absolute submission to divine powers as in monotheism – Judaism, Christianity and Islam as well as Sikhism– or in multi-theism such as Hinduism and so forth. His study also indicates that by that time atheism and agnosticism will be the dominant spiritual doctrines worldwide. In fact, he claims that atheism is already a firmly established moral doctrine in many developed countries.

Such radical and bold predictions – whether evaluated by valid statistical methods or not – will raise the eyebrows of many people. How could one say with absolute certainty on the outcome of the religious and non-religious population when there are so many complex issues and interleaving socio-economic and political dynamics involved? Nonetheless, it is worthwhile to look into the broad outline of the study and try to get the flavour of his reasoning behind such predictions about believers.

Worldwide there are nearly 4,500 million adherents of all religions – monotheistic and multi-theistic beliefs put together – out of the total global human population of just over 7,500 million. In other words, nearly 60 per cent of the human population are now believers and 40 per cent are non-believers – agnostics, atheist and other 'unaffiliated' causes. The breakdown of the 4,500 million adherents of beliefs is approximately like this: Christianity – 1,850 million; Islam – 1,550 million; Hinduism – 1,000 million; Sikhism – 20 million and Judaism – 15 million and other smaller religions around the world – 65 million. (These numbers of religious followers are at variance with the numbers quoted in other articles, which were taken from various religious books.)

*Figure 3.9   Religious Symbols: Yin Yang (Eastern Spirituality,
1 o'clock), Hinduism (Om, 3 o'clock), Christianity (Cross, 4 o'clock),
Buddhism (Chakra, 6 o'clock), Sikhism (Khanda, 7 o'clock), Judaism
(Star of David, 9 o'clock), Islam (crescent moon and star, 11 o'clock)*

The trends in believers' number in various religions are not
the same. Some religions like Christianity (Protestant) and
Judaism are increasing at a very low rate and in some places, they
are not increasing at all. Hinduism is increasing at a
progressively slower rate. But Islam and Catholicism are
expanding at somewhat higher rates than the world population
growth rate. But behind these trends there are complex interconnections of the socio-economic conditions of the believers
which influence the trends.

However, the above hypothesis of Nigel Barber has been
contradicted by a political scientist, Eric Kaufmann, who holds

the view that the proportion of religious people is unlikely to come down as believers tend to have more children than non-believers. In Roman Catholicism, birth control is either banned or discouraged on the pretext that if God gives a child, who are we to stop it? In Islam, a similar view is held in most of the Islamic states. In some oil-rich Islamic states, large families are actively encouraged as they don't want to be outnumbered by expatriate workers in their own countries. In India, family planning is despised on moral grounds. Mrs Indira Gandhi lost the national election simply because she encouraged birth control! The biotechnologist Thomas Rees concurs with Eric Kaufmann and even holds the view that religious people may even have a higher proportion of the population in future simply because of believers' higher birth rates.

So where is the evidence that believers' numbers are coming down? Nigel Barber dismisses the higher birth rate evidence by saying that as the world prospers, the present-day believers, mostly poorer people, will have fewer children as women will go out to work. The women will become materially conscious and hence will have smaller family sizes. There is some evidence of this in Bangladesh and India where family prosperity and comfort have become more important than the number of children in the family. In having this attitude, there must be sufficient employment opportunity and economic prosperity, not only collectively but also individually. The reverse of this attitude is in evidence in Pakistan where the economy is in decline (in relative terms) and the population is soaring.

The irony is that as people become more numinous, they tend to neglect their efforts to improve their economic conditions. They even sacrifice their diminishing resources in the name of God, so that they can get better returns from God in future. Many people go to Hajj selling their last piece of land or even borrowing money in the hope that God will reward them adequately, preferably in this world and, if not, definitely in the next world!

230

So, it seems there is a correlation, or to be exact an inverse correlation, between the economic performance of a state and its population growth. In Western developed countries, population growth is small because the indigenous population is more involved in family prosperity than in the increase in family size. The only increase in population in those countries is due to net population migration to the country and the higher birth rate of the migrant population. The decreasing trend in population is also discernible in well-run economies such as Singapore, Malaysia and so forth, where liberal immigration policies are not pursued.

In addition to the population increase of religious people, there is another factor that is worth considering and that is religious conversion. When poor, deprived people of the underclasses are given a helping hand by the religious preachers, they tend to embrace and adopt that religion and enjoy the benefits. Islam is having a good run on this account. Also, poor but religiously moderate Muslim men and women having help and support from Islamic organisations would tend to be closely associated with those Islamic organisations, who happen to be radical but socially responsible Islamic groups. This trend of radicalisation of the population is evident in many Islamic countries including Pakistan, Bangladesh and many African countries.

With all these factors interacting with each other, it is difficult to make a definite statement as to whether the believer numbers or the proportion of believer numbers will go up or down in relation to non-believers. But one thing is certain, that believers will perform relatively badly in social, economic and other ladders in relation to non-believers. This is already evident in developed countries as well as developing countries. Between the countries, non-believer countries are relatively richer than believer countries.

There are, of course, some exceptions, but those exceptions have nothing to do with religion. Some believer countries such

231

as Middle Eastern countries may be richer than non-believer countries only because they get wealth from natural resources such as petroleum, mineral resources etc. The gratitude of the people for getting wealth from nowhere goes to the divine authority and their religiosity increases as a result. Whether that religiosity will last for very long is an open question. As the citizens of those countries become educated and enlightened, they are likely to be exposed to modern science and technology and they may start questioning whether God has anything to do with the natural reserve they have got. At that point, the tipping point for their numinosity will come.

The net outcome of this social-religious-economic tussle is that poor people – whether in developed or developing countries – become poorer as they embrace religion more and the rich people become richer as they give up religion. There are, of course, other factors which come into play at individual or collective levels. But religion singularly has a detrimental effect on individual or collective economic performance.

The numbers of believers as against non-believers depend in the final analysis on the economic performance of the individuals as well as of the State. A clear separation of believer and non-believer countries, somewhat similar to the so-called north-south divide, may arise. However, as the north is rich and educated, it is most likely to be populated by non-believers. As these northern people pursue pleasure and leisure in life, as against family expansion, the total population size is unlikely to go up significantly. On the other hand, the south, being poor and inhabited by relatively uneducated people, will see a significant increase in population size and most of them will cling to one or the other religion. Thus, believer numbers are likely to increase faster than non-believer numbers. So, there is no evidence or scenario that religion will disappear within a matter of 25 to 30 years. On the contrary, religion is likely to gain an even stronger foothold on the world population.

The regressive world of Islam

The world of Islam is in a state of turmoil. Radicalised Muslims and their misdemeanours are rarely out of the media spotlight these days, around the whole world, and rightly so.

From the earth shattering events of 9/11 in New York in 2001 and the London Underground bombing in 2005 to al-Qaeda activities in Iraq, Afghanistan, Syria and many other places; the atrocities of the so-called *Islamic State (IS)* in beheading countless innocents in Syria and Iraq; Boko Haram's kidnapping and killing of school-children in Nigeria; the killing of Charlie Hebdo employees in France; and the killing of 23 tourists in the Bardo Museum in Tunis by the IS affiliate groups and many, many more; all point to the grim reality that there is something fundamentally wrong with these radicalised Muslims and their deviant mentality.

Figure 3.10   *Victims of an attack by gunmen in Tunisia's national museum in Tunis on 18 March 2015*

233

These people are just not in harmony with modern times and utterly fail to uphold human values. But before one jumps to conclusions in apportioning blame to all Muslims in a sweeping generalisation, one must apply common sense. One must consider that Muslims all over the world do not belong to a single race, single culture and single language although they may uphold a single religious trait.

There are divergences and disharmony among the adherents of Islam as much as in any other major religion. There are more than 1.65 billion Muslims (over 21 per cent of the world population) scattered all over the world and in all continents. Hence it is well-nigh impossible to collectively box them together and apportion collective responsibility.

From the deserts of the Middle East and North Africa to the lush green swamps of Malaysia and Indonesia; from the Himalayan Mountain range, through the Alps, to the Baltic Sea; from the deserts of Mexico to the icy vastness of Canada; Muslims have found their homes. These Muslims are by no means a homogenous group – either in race or language, culture, socio-economic conditions, educational levels, behavioural pattern and so forth.

However, one trait that may be seen to embrace them all is the religion of Islam. Even then, it does not mean all Muslims embraced the religion equally or are engulfed in its devotion deeply – their religiosity encompasses 'born Muslims' (meaning nothing more than sheer Muslim ancestry), atheist Muslims, agnostic Muslims, secular Muslims, all the way to devout Muslims incorporating fundamentalists, Jihadists, and other diehard Islamists. The first group (from born Muslims to secular Muslims) may not be in the majority, but they represent the educated and cultured class of Muslims, and they are deadly opposed to the barbarities perpetrated by the radicalised Muslims of the last group.

Figure 3.11   A typical niqab-wearing Muslim woman

Studies leading to deep introspection of the causes of egregious behaviour of radicalised Muslims have been carried out by various erudite Muslims and religious scholars with specific objectives but have resulted in no clear findings. However, one study, which has drawn the rapt attention of the public recently, was carried out by a Danish psychologist, Dr Nicolai Sennels, in which he addressed this challenging issue of Muslim fanaticism from two divergent angles: (a) genetic considerations, and (b) religious and cultural considerations. I will consider both of these points and try to make an objective judgement from the layman's point of view.

The first point that Dr Sennels asserts is that the gene pool of Muslims has become corrupt due to the inbreeding of Muslims, not now, but right from the beginning of the religion! This smacks of a strong resonance to the Nazi 'eugenics' philosophy which claimed that the Jews are of lower human breed due to inbreeding among cousins of the Jews. This concocted philosophy offered the Nazis a justification for exterminating Jews, because lower breed humans would have no place among the German Aryans!

Now Sennels, more than 70 years later, has picked up that discredited and abhorrent racist narrative, and hypothesised that because of inter-marriages between first cousins or second cousins among the Muslims, the offspring suffer from recessive genetic disorders and, since that practice had been going on for nearly 1400 years, the Muslim gene pool is irreversibly damaged. He even went on to say that nearly 50% of all Muslims suffer from genetic disorders!

Firstly, this so-called extensive inbreeding between first cousins of Muslims is not widespread at all and is limited to ultra-conservative tribal groups. Sennels' quoted statistics that in Pakistan it is nearly 70%; in Saudi Arabia it is 67%; in Jordan it is 64% and so on, are baseless and without any foundation. The figures are not only wrong, but they are wrong by significant margins. Secondly, even if there is the inbreeding, there is no certainty that the DNA will be defective and that the offspring will suffer genetic disorders. The genetic disorder is basically stochastic i.e. probabilistic in nature. It has been found statistically that birth defects increase from the baseline figure of 3-4 per cent to 4-7 per cent from inbreeding. Thus, this marginal increase is not that significant as to warrant generic condemnation of the gene pool.

The second main point that Sennels propounds – religious and cultural consideration – bears more weight and is worthy of assessment here. In his book, which he most mendaciously calls, 'Criminal Muslims: A Psychologist's Experiences from the Copenhagen Municipality,' he presumes that Muslims' cultural and religious propensity played a central role in their psychological development and criminal behaviour.

He identified 'anger', 'locus of control,' and 'Muslim identity' as the three most important indicators which differentiate Muslims from other religious groups. He asserts that in any discussion in the West, expression of 'anger', loss of temper and threatening behaviour are considered uncivilised, an indication of losing the argument, and bad behaviour. But in Islamic culture, anger, loss of temper, physical threats et cetera are considered assertive and establish valid points forcefully and hence perfectly acceptable. In conflicts and social disputes, if a Muslim does not respond aggressively, he is considered weak and is viewed as upholding dubious points.

(From my personal experience, I can say that in Saudi Arabia if there is a traffic accident, the person who can shout most and make the most aggressive gestures showing his outrage is the non-guilty party. So, immediately after the accident, there is a shouting match, aggressive behaviour and threatening gestures, regardless of what had happened or who did what. This behavioural pattern percolates from Bedouin culture to the Muslim psyche. On the other hand, in the West the two parties calmly exchange their details such as vehicle numbers, insurance policies et cetera, and if necessary, call the police and matters follow smoothly thereon without any violence).

This anger-led threat leads to violence and even death. In the Islamic world, a simple argument or a disagreement can escalate into physical violence and even fatality, as no one wants to lose face or prestige in front of others, and that is the culture. This is how the 'blood-feud' comes into tribal Muslim tradition. In the West, discussion, dialogue, compromise et cetera are all peaceful means of dispute resolution before going, if necessary, into the lap of the law.

The second point he mentions is the 'locus of control.' The locus of control is a psychological term which describes people's feelings and experiences, and whether internal or external factors influence their lives.

In the West, people feel that their lives are influenced by internal factors which emanate from within i.e. from themselves. People control their motivation, ways of thinking, points of view, their emotions and their communication. In short, they take control of their lives.

In the Islamic world, people feel that the external 'locus of control' influences them. Every action, every statement is adjunct with 'Inshallah,' meaning 'Allah willing'. People thus relegate their responsibilities, their accountability, their future course of action on the external factor – if Allah wishes, it will happen, otherwise not. Conversely, if something untoward happened, it must have been due to Allah's sanction! The downside of dependence on 'unknown' external factors is that religious leaders can masquerade as agents of the external factor and interpret or impose their concocted views on the people.

Thus, Muslims may become over-reliant on the transmission of external factors through intermediaries and gradually become automatons – they lose capacity to think independently or rationally for themselves, as they see themselves as mere agents to carry out instructions. On top of that, Muslims see life on earth as nothing more than a test bed – eternal heaven or hell awaits them - so every action in compliance with the external factor must be carried out here on earth.

The third point which Sennels mentions is the 'Muslim identity'. He says that Muslims cling to Muslim identity very strongly, primarily because they are constantly reminded of their 'Muslim-ness' by Imams, family heads, and social leaders. Even when Muslims emigrate to a new country, the Muslim identity remains more important than the adopted national identity. They tend to show off their religious identity by distinctive attire such as the burqa, niqab, and hijab. They either refuse to integrate or fail to integrate with the host community no matter how long they live in that country.

There may be a number of factors that contribute to such behaviour. The most important one is that Muslims of national groups tend to stick together, follow their customs together, and mix only with other Muslims in mosques and on religious occasions. By doing so, they don't feel the need to integrate with the host community. They fail to learn the local language, culture, and etiquette and they feel unwelcome by the host community. This disjointed existence creates mutual apathy and antagonism. The younger generation even feels inbuilt anger and revolts against the host society.

This identity issue was not a problem with other religious groups such as the Jews who emigrated from East European countries in large numbers to England and America immediately before or after the Second World War. They assimilated so well that after one or two generations, it is now difficult to separate them from the indigenous population. Hindus, Sikhs and other religious groups make positive efforts to integrate with the host community, but not so by the Muslims.

Nicolai Sennels' attempt to explain Muslim fanaticism on the basis of gene defects does not carry any weight at all. Based on dubious statistics, flawed logic and lack of risk assessment methodology, he came to a conclusion that only reflects his conviction and blatant racist outlook.

However, his deliberations on religious and cultural considerations are much more credible and worthy of serious considerations. What this consideration brings out subtly is that the religion of Islam needs to be reformed. Without such reform this religion would be perpetually at odds with the norm of modern society. Although Islam is the newest of the three major monotheistic religions, it is singularly overburdened with unreformed theological narratives, which other religions have gradually adjusted. One may consider that these religions came into being when human civilisation was at its infancy, when the Earth was assumed to be flat, the Sun was perceived to go round the Earth, and Heaven and Hell were just beyond the northern star. All of these concepts have found their way into Judaism, Christianity, and then to Islam.

With the advancement of science and technology, it has been found that many of the revelations in religions were at odds with modern development. However, Judaism and Christianity have over the centuries subtly adjusted and reinterpreted revelations to accommodate those scientific views as far as possible. The head of the Roman Catholic Church, Pope Francis, said recently, *"The big bang, which we hold to be the origin of the world, does not contradict the intervention of the divine creator but rather requires it. Evolution in nature is not inconsistent with the notion of Creation because evolution requires the creation of beings that evolve."*

But Islam refused to reform and steadfastly clung on to its original version of the divine message. This assertion of absoluteness is the root cause of conflict between Islam and the modern world.

The brutality of religious fanatics

Another most barbaric, most heinous crime was committed by religious fanatics in the name of Islam in full view of the public (as well as of law-enforcing officers) on the streets of Dhaka. Dr Avijit Kumar Roy, a bioengineer working in software engineering in the USA, was brutally murdered as he and his wife were going home at about 9pm on Thursday 26th February 2015, having attended the *Ekushey* Book Fair and launching his newly published books.

Figure 3.12   Writer and bioengineer, Avijit Roy, murdered by Muslim extremists in 2015

They were attacked by two or three assailants with machetes, and he was hacked to death. The coroner at the Dhaka Medical College Hospital, only a short distance away from the crime scene, testified that the attack was an act of professional killers. Two deep rooted stabs at the back of the skull were so severe that the victim died within a short time from severe bleeding. His wife had also been attacked and she was in critical condition.

So, what did Avijit Roy, a software engineer, an author, and a blogger do to warrant such a vicious attack by these murderous men? Avijit Roy and his Muslim wife came to Bangladesh from America only a week earlier with the specific purpose of launching his books on *Biswasher Virus (The Virus of Faith)* and *Sunyo theke Mahabiswa (From Nothing to the Universe)* in the Ekushey Book Fair. *The Virus of Faith* was his latest book.

The content of the book, *The Virus of Faith* is nothing new, and no derogatory comment on Islam in particular is present. It deals with the overall obsessive behavioural pattern with spiritual or divine doctrinaire, which may be dubbed as a spell, which leads people to become blindly numinous and obsessive. This numinosity is not restricted to any particular religion; it is prevalent in all religions and to all religious minded people.

The American Philosopher and polemicist, Daniel C. Dennett, in his book *Breaking the Spell* advanced the subtlety of Darwin's survival instinct – a behavioural pattern which may apparently be viewed as contradictory to the survival instinct, but there is a deep rooted, almost covert survival drive. He gave an example of ants in the meadow which perpetually try to climb up the blade of a grass. The ant may fall down but it would try again to climb. This strenuous effort of the ant is counter-intuitive to the survival instinct, as the ant in the grass may be devoured by a sheep or a cow and hence no survival benefit accrues to the ant. But there may be a hidden survival instinct of something else overriding that of ants.

The brain of the ant has been commandeered by a tiny parasite that needs to get into the guts of the animal to complete its reproductive cycle. The ant simply acts as a vehicle for the parasites. A similar, but not exactly the same, trend is observable in humankind. A strong incentive, an obsessive feeling, a blinding fear in the human mind, can occasionally become so overpowering that the normal biological function in a human

242

being may become somewhat redundant. The basic biological function that is carried out under instructions from normal 'genes' in various organs and tissues may be overtaken in human brains by *'memes'* mimicking genes.

The concept of 'memes', similar to genes, has been advanced by Professor Richard Dawkins (Oxford Professor in Evolutionary Biology). Once this 'meme' gets into the brain, it can mutate, it can reinforce itself and drive or manipulate human behaviour. Once it is infected, it grows like a virus.

Avijit Roy took up this theme and elaborated it in his book. It is simply a hypothesis, which can be applied to all other spheres of human activities, besides religion. For example, when someone falls in love, madly in love; love is the only thing that matters in life at that point to that person. Quite often, the boy would say that he would not live without her. His brain signal has become so strong and overpowering that all other competing signals, such as biological needs, social pressure et cetera become temporarily dysfunctional.

Another example may be that occasionally a man can become totally obsessed with money. He wants more and more money, which we may call utter greed. He may want more money than he can possibly spend in his lifetime; but that does not stop him from wanting more; his brain has become infected with the greed virus.

Avijit articulated this type of behavioural pattern in his book and the Islamic fundamentalists found this too much to tolerate, despite the fact that there was nothing in the book that was particularly against Islam. This virus of faith can grow in Hinduism, Christianity, Judaism and so forth. Indeed, when it does grow it produces a corresponding pool of fundamentalists. So why did the Islamic fanatics take such strong exception to this idea as to warrant the termination of his life? Has life become so cheap to them, that they can eliminate it at their pleasure? Or do they feel that they are so strong that any dissenting voice is unworthy of being allowed to live on Earth? What sort of human

243

value do they propagate when they carry out their barbaric act in the name of Islam?

Undoubtedly, this act of murdering a man for proposing or supporting an idea is most heinous, to say the least. An Islamic organisation by the name of Ansar Bangla 7 has purportedly claimed the responsibility for this crime. This is not the first time or the sole incident when the Islamic organisation had carried out such barbaric acts. In Bangladesh alone, a number of bloggers, including Ahmed Rajib Haider in February 2013, as well as a prominent author and educationist, Humayun Azad, in 2004, were killed by Islamic assailants in similar fashion. There are innumerable other cases where religious intolerance directly leads to the murder of individuals!

Worldwide, Islamic fundamentalists have become so completely insane that it is indescribable and inexplicable. From the 9/11 attack killing over 3000 people, the London underground attack killing 38 people, to attacks in Mumbai, Madrid, Mali, Bali, London, Brussels and so on by Islamists, all are extremely shameful to the religion. The internecine conflicts between Sunnis and Shias all over the world only bring disgrace to the religion. The beheading of nurses, news reporters, voluntary workers, as well as innocent men, women and children by ISIS in the Middle East in the name of Islam, does not bring any good name to the religion. Is Islam so very fragile that any question, however remotely associated with Islam, has to be violently suppressed? No other religion has such a vicious, violent attitude. Is it not time that mullahs and preachers advocating violence take a good look at themselves and analyse their behaviour and see how they fit in the modern world?

Jinnah's Pakistan …. Seventy-three years on

Figure 3.13   Muhammad Ali Jinnah, the founder of Pakistan

Last August (2020), India and Pakistan celebrated their independence from the British Raj, seventy-three years ago. In some paradoxical way, Bangladesh also joined in half-heartedly in that celebration as that was also the precursor to her own independence, some 24 years later on 26th March 1971.

The *Two Nation Theory (TNT)* was adopted and promoted in the late 1930s and 1940s by Muhammad Ali Jinnah with so much hullabaloo that not only the Indian National Congress (INC) but also the British Raj, shaken and grievously injured and weakened by WWII, had to cave in. The strident call for a separate state for the minority Muslims comprising some 30 per cent of the Indian population was nothing but Jinnah's Machiavellian ploy to achieve his political ambition. After spending the formative years of his political career in the Congress, Jinnah realised that

245

his ambition to reach the highest rung of the political ladder in the talent-strewn Congress could not possibly be achieved. So, he had to find alternative avenues to achieve his goals.

For centuries Hindus, Muslims, Sikhs, Buddhists, Jains, Christians, Zoroastrians, Jews and all other religious adherents had been living together sometimes under Muslim rules, sometimes under Hindu rules, sometimes under Christian rules and many a time under an admixture of rules. But never before were people segregated on the pretext that minorities would not receive justice under a joint and unified government. Maulana Abul Kalam Azad, the INC president for a number of terms, Mahatma Gandhi and many others tried to persuade Jinnah to be part of a united India by offering him various options, such as a Federal State for India with all administrative powers except foreign and defence being vested in states, Jinnah's choice in the matter of first Federal Cabinet, etc. But Jinnah would have none of it.

The country was divided into two nations – one for the Muslims and the other for all religious denominations in India. Pakistan was formed by putting together two Muslim majority areas – West Pakistan on the west and East Pakistan on the east of India – separated by nearly 1,500 km of Indian territory. There was no commonality between these two peoples, except the tenuous link of Islam. If Islam could be the glue between various peoples, then the whole of the Middle East would have been a single state, which it is not!

However, Jinnah won the day, not so much by the strength of his political argument but by sheer communal animosity and barbarity. When communalism is stoked up by politicians to gain currency, race riots inevitably follow. More than one million people – men, women and children – died in race riots immediately pre- and post-independence and ten million people were displaced.

That the new state would look after the interests of the Muslims sounds totally hollow. More than 30% of Muslims

246

remained in India despite some of the most horrendous race riots triggered by politicians to polarise the country. Jinnah used Islam for his political purposes, but he was not a practising Muslim at all. He belonged to the Ismaili sect (also known as Aga Khani) — part of the Shia sect in Islam. He was a thoroughbred western educated lawyer with a western lifestyle. When he formed the first government in Pakistan, his first foreign minister, Muhammad Zafrullah Khan, was an Ahmadi (also known as Qadiani), another sect of the Shia community, now regarded by Sunnis as heretical. His law minister was a Hindu. Jinnah's second wife was a Zoroastrian, an ancient religion predating all monotheistic religions. So, religion was definitely not the deciding factor, although the state was created on this basis.

However, within a few short months of the creation of Pakistan, Islamists led by the Jamaat-e-Islam saw their opportunity. The first step to transform Pakistan into an Islamic state was taken by Liaquat Ali Khan, the first prime minister, through the Objectives Resolution, wherein it was declared that sovereignty over the entire universe belonged to God Almighty! All non-religious activities were gradually discouraged in both wings of the country. Within a few years, Pakistan was declared an Islamic Republic.

Religious fanaticism had completely taken over Pakistan since the 1970s. If such fanaticism had existed in Pakistan when it was created, then Mohammad Ali Jinnah, the founding father of Pakistan, would have been declared non-Muslim and expelled from the country. Mohammad Zafrullah Khan would have been relieved of his duties as the country's top diplomat and imprisoned on charges of heresy. Professor Abdus Salam, the first Muslim Nobel Laureate in physics from Pakistan, had actually been stripped of his nationality and declared a non-Muslim as he was an Ahmadi. His tombstone was desecrated by removing the word 'Muslim' from it.

The very ideology of the two-nation theory now stands totally hollow, non-sensical and discredited. Those two nations have now spawned into three nations, Bangladesh being the latest one. As it stands now Baloch, Sindh and the border regions in Pakistan are asserting their rights based on their ethnicity and cultural identity in contrast to Pakistan's assertion of religiosity. If you open a can of worms, it is very difficult to put the worms back in.

The communal ideology of one state, one religion is not only heinous but positively dangerous also. Pakistan as well as most, if not all, Muslim countries, started driving away non-Muslims from the country. The more fanatical a country is, the more ethnic cleansing it carries out. In 1950 (shortly after independence), West Pakistan (now Pakistan) had 85.5% Muslims, whereas by 2010, the percentage had gone up to 96.5%, meaning the non-Muslim population had been reduced from 14.5% to 3.5%. In 1950, East Pakistan (now Bangladesh) had an 85% Muslim population, whereas in 2010 it had gone up to 89.6%. Contrast that with India, a non-Muslim country, where the Muslim population between these two dates went up from 10% to 13.5%. In most Middle Eastern Muslim countries, the Muslim population is 98% to 99%, with all non-Muslims having been driven out or eliminated!

Intolerance is the hallmark of Pakistani politicians. In 1971 when Zulfiqar Ali Bhutto roared that he would never play second fiddle to Sheikh Mujibur Rahman (although Mujib had the largest number of elected representatives in the proposed assembly), one could not miss echoes of Jinnah's strident call in the 1940 Lahore Resolution for a Muslim homeland for Muslim people (with him as the leader).

Disturbing streaks of personal ambition are self-evident in Pakistani politics. In Pakistan, not a single elected prime minister since independence had managed to serve his or her full term. The hands of the military authorities were present all over the place. Democracy has never been allowed to flourish in Pakistan even after seventy-three years of independence. Chaos and confusion reign everywhere, law and order are blatantly absent. If this is not the sign of a failed state, what is it? As the Indian politician Shashi Tharoor once said, *"The state of India has an army, the army of Pakistan has a state."*

Bangladesh is fortunate enough to have parted company with Pakistan within 24 years of a most unhappy relationship. How dreadful it would have been if Bangladesh had been with Pakistan now! But unless Bangladeshi people wipe away entirely that dreadful association and vouch never to entertain any thought of association with Pakistani Islamists, the nightmare may well come back.

Mind-boggling Saudi mendacity

Saudi Arabia portrays itself as the holiest place in the whole of the Muslim world of 54 sovereign states and claims to be the custodian of the two most sacred mosques in Islam. But the reality cannot be further from such exalted claims. The country is beset with corruption, misogyny, brutality, inhumanity, deception and downright criminality. No country in the whole world can match or even come close to Saudi Arabia's egregious claim of virtuosity and the reality of unfettered criminality.

Let us scrutinise Saudi Arabia's activities in modern times and the havoc these activities are creating worldwide. To do so, we have to start from the roots of Saudi Arabia, its barbaric activities, its total absence of humanity and its criminal use of religion for political purposes. Overall, this country wants to gain prominence and supremacy at the back of religion and to do so, nothing is off the table.

The Kingdom of Saudi Arabia came into being in 1932 when Abdulaziz ibn Saud managed to beat his rival, Ikhwan, in the battle of Sabilla in 1930 with the covert support of Britain and named the country after his family name, Saud. In other words, the country became the possession of the Saud dynasty. The country and the people were extremely impoverished at that time. But as luck would have it, in 1938 a vast reserve of oil was discovered in areas close to the Persian Gulf by a British oil company. As petrodollars started pouring in, the country prospered, despite blatant corruption. The oil revenue in 2019 was $202 billion, despite the oil price being less than half of what it was a year ago.

Saudi Arabia's objectives with its vast oil wealth rests on two main planks: (i) legitimising and securing the rule of ibn Saud over the country and (ii) gaining undisputed supremacy in the Islamic world by eliminating any vestiges of dissent to their Sunni sect from other religious sects in Islam. Needless to say

251

that Islam, being the political religion, readily lends itself to use overtly and covertly to achieve the above mentioned objectives of the Saudi Sunni dynasty.

When Abdulaziz ibn Saud conquered Riyadh in 1902 by sheer brutality, he realised that the fractious regions of the desert lands of Arabia could only be brought together under his control if the overarching umbrella of religion was established - an uncanny resemblance of what Prophet Mohammed felt some 1400 years earlier. He revived an alliance drawn between Mohammad ibn Saud (the founder of the 1st Saud dynasty) and the preacher Abd-al Wahhab in 1744 whereby ibn Saud and his heirs pledged to protect the Wahhabi dynasty from the prevailing animosity towards it in exchange of retaining the proprietary right over this Wahhabi ideology by the Saudis. This Wahhabi ideology mirrored the original teachings of Islam as encoded in Salafism, but with more vitriol and viciousness. It suited Abdulaziz ibn-Saud and his band of warrior Islamicists very well to use Wahhabism/Salafism as a tool to impose autocracy in the name of Islam. Thus, Islam became truly a political-military religion.

What ISIL/IS did in Iraq, Syria and elsewhere reflect in totality the Wahhabi ideology which Saudi Arabia propagated and promoted. A few beheadings by IS on camera of 'infidels' might have shocked the world; but in Saudi Arabia beheadings of human beings on offences like adultery, apostasy, heresy, insult to prophet Muhammad etc. are almost an everyday affair. These are all done in Saudi Arabia legitimately under the *Sharia Law*. That the brutality of Sharia Law conflicts with the Human Rights Provisions to which Saudi Arabia had signed up to does not bother them an iota. Law is what suits the interests of the ruling class in Saudi Arabia; not something that conflicts with their interests.

It may be mentioned that the political Islam, reflecting the Bedouin culture of the 7th century in the deserts of Arabia, lends a very good helping hand to those bigoted men. As per religion, women are not to be treated equal to men. In fact, in matters of

252

inheritance, a daughter is exactly half of a son. A woman cannot divorce her husband at all in Islam, but a man can divorce his wife by pronouncing 'divorce' words three times. If a woman is raped, it is always the fault of the woman – on the grounds that she might have aroused sexuality in the man and hence she is the one to be punished. Many hundreds of migrant women workers in Saudi Arabia and other Gulf Countries are punished every year by long term imprisonment, severe lashing or even beheading when their masters happen to rape them. For fear of their lives, these women workers remain silent. But if they become pregnant, they have to face brutal punishment as prescribed by the Wahhabi ideology.

Saudi Arabia's other objective is the global domination of Sunni Wahhabism. As the King of Saudi Arabia is the custodian of the two holiest mosques in Islam, Sunni domination is effectively his domination. The war in Yemen that is going on since 2014 is due to Saudi Arabia's attack on Houthi rebels who are mainly Shias. Saudi Arabia had been bombing various parts of the country to kill Houthi rebels and any fatality of innocent civilians was regarded as collateral damage. More than 233,000 civilians have died up to the end of 2020 due to the Saudi-led coalition attacks on Yemen, according to the UN Humanitarian Office. Millions of children are now facing serious malnutrition and death due to diseases.

Saudi Arabia and its cohorts in the Gulf Cooperation Council (Bahrain, Kuwait, Oman, UAE, Qatar and Saudi Arabia) have been funding and fuelling the discontent among the Syrian people against the *Alawite regime* of Bashar al-Assad. Alawite belongs to the Shiite sect of Islam, which Saudi Arabia regards as the enemy of Sunni. Other Shiite denominations such as Ismaili, Zaidi, Baha'is and Ahmadiyya are also Wahhabis/Salafist enemies. Sufi has been declared non-Muslim. ISIL/IS had been killing these apostates under their occupation, unless they accept Sunni ideology straightaway.

Saudi Arabia is the root of most of the evils, if not all, of the world today. Most of the attackers of the World Trade Centre in New York in 2001 were Saudi fundamentalists. The untold misery of millions of people in Syria, Iraq and other places was due to Saudi-inspired rebellion against established regimes. Despite that, the country did not feel any compassion to offer refuge to the dispossessed war victims, although the country has hundreds of billions of dollars and vast unused tracts of land. Saudi and other Wahhabi regimes in the Middle East gave the Fatwah that women (and even girls over 10 or 11) would be required to wear the face veil (hijab) and the all-body veil (burqa) as part of the religious requirement. And now hundreds of millions of women round the world wear these attires, although there is nowhere in the religious books that states they are mandatory.

Figure 3.14   Jamal Khashoggi's son was summoned by Crown Prince Mohammad bin Salman to express his condolence. However, an American Intelligence report showed that Mohammad bin Salman ordered Khashoggi's killing.

In 2018, a Saudi dissident journalist Jamal Khashoggi who worked for the Washington Post was killed in the Saudi Consulate in Istanbul, Turkey. He advocated liberalisation of the strict Wahhabi doctrine in Saudi Arabia and in the process became an enemy of crown prince Mohammad bin Salman. When Khashoggi went to the Saudi consulate in Istanbul to collect his marriage certificate on 2nd October 2018, the death squad was waiting for him. He was murdered, his body was chopped up into pieces and then dumped into the well of the Consul General's home just across the road. They also enacted an elaborate ploy with one look-alike Khashoggi leaving the consulate through the back door.

When Khashoggi did not come out of the consulate hours later, his fiancée (a Turkish national) started enquiring. The Saudi Consulate said at first that they knew nothing about Khashoggi's whereabouts and when she contacted high level Turkish officials, then they said he had left through the back door and produced a video clip to support it. That was a video of an imposter of Khashoggi, as reporters found out that the imposter was wearing different shoes and a different tie. The Turkish government investigated the case and found that Khashoggi had been brutally murdered inside the consulate. Two weeks later, the Saudi government admitted that he was killed in a fight inside the consulate. How could a man be killed inside the consulate, while consulate officials were unaware of it?

Recently, under the presidency of Joe Biden, the hitherto hidden American Intelligence report that was produced in 2018 under Donald Trump was released and it stated quite clearly that he was murdered inside the consulate by the direct orders of crown prince Mohammad bin Salman. For over two years, the Saudi government had been lying and deceiving the world and Donald Trump was complicit with it.

There is a rhetorical quip which asks, "When do you know that an Arab is lying?" The answer comes, "When he opens his mouth."

Should Britain consider banning the Niqab and Burqa?

There is a controversy as to what Islam directs women to wear. Some religious scholars argue that the *hijab* is obligatory, whereas others disagree and assert that the *burqa* or *niqab* is. Before considering the issue of religious obligation on wearing the burqa or niqab as claimed by some devout followers of Islam, let us look at different attires that are stated to have been specified in the Quran and Hadith. The 'burqa' is a garment for women to envelop the whole of the woman's body, from head to toe, with a mesh cloth over the part of the eyes to see. A burqa is normally made of black cloth, though recently other colours are also used. A 'niqab' is similar to a burqa but with a thin slit, instead of mesh cloth, for the eyes. A niqab is also predominantly black in colour. The 'hijab' is, on the other hand, a headgear that is wrapped around the head covering the head, neck and shoulders with only the face exposed.

But the fact is that women in the Arab Peninsula used to wear the niqab and burqa well before Islam came into existence. Islam embraced that practice as a continuation of prevailing customs. There is no unambiguous religious call directing Muslim women to wear the niqab or burqa. With regard to the hijab, Prophet Mohammad wanted only his wives to wear a hijab to distinguish them from other women and to indicate to other people to show respect to them. There was no obligation in the religious edicts to copy Mohammad's wives' attire.

So why do some Muslim women (and men) living in the West (as well as in the East) now feel and claim that it is a religious obligation for women to wear a niqab or burqa or some other similar attire? How and why did these religious obligations surface now, which were not there even 30 years ago? Does the claim of infringement of human rights to conceal women in public by covering themselves from head-to-toe stack up? Isn't this concealment itself an infringement of human rights, as it arguably epitomises the servitude of women to men and thereby breaches sexual equality?

The Universal Declaration of Human Rights (UDHR) was framed by the Human Rights Commission at the end of World War II and was adopted by the United Nations General Assembly in 1948. In the preamble of the declaration, it stated that "*in recognition of the inherent dignity and of the equal and inalienable rights of all members of the human family*", this declaration had been adopted. It covered various aspects of human rights such as rights to education, health, liberty, security, nationality and above all human dignity. This convention was signed by 48 states at that time, but Saudi Arabia and some other orthodox Muslim states refused to sign it as they disagreed with Article 16 (which dealt with '*equal rights to men and women in marriage*') on grounds of religion. In Islam, women are subservient to men in marriage – both in status and family hierarchy. However, in 2008, the Organisation of Islamic Conference (OIC) accepted the human rights convention and so the extreme fundamentalist countries, being members of the OIC, have adopted *de facto* the provisions of the UDHR.

Niqab   Burqa

Figure 3.15   *Proclaimed Islamic attire – Niqab and Burqa*

But, in reality, most of these Muslim countries have been flouting, to varying degrees, the human rights of women and have opted surreptitiously to adhere to religious edicts. In Islam, women are required to be confined within the homes of their parents and then of their husbands. Women are not allowed to go out in public without being accompanied by their fathers or brothers and after marriage by their husbands. Women are not allowed to be educated beyond the basic levels to read, write and keep accounts of family expenses. Women are not allowed to drive (modern interpretation by Saudi *Wahhabism*). Men and women are not treated as equal in Islam – women inherit half of what a man can inherit; women are subservient to men (husbands) in the family; husbands can divorce wives at will (without showing any cause), but women cannot. Men can marry four times and keep four wives concurrently. Women are kept indoors and when they go out with their husbands, they are to be fully veiled (according to some). And so, giving 'equal rights to men and women in marriage' arguably goes against a basic foundation of Sharia law.

So, with a background situation like this, when devout Muslims assert that denying untrammelled rights to wear a niqab or burqa is unacceptable, as it is an infringement of their human rights, one finds it rather bizarre; particularly when so many other human rights are denied in Islam. There are a number of issues which need to be considered when addressing the pros and cons of allowing the burqa and niqab to be worn by Muslim women and these are:

If Muslim women are religiously so orthodox to feel obligated to wear these attires, they should not defy other obligations in Islam such as not going out of their homes without being accompanied by their fathers or husbands. Even if such attires are perceived to be obligatory, it is notable that many such adherents selectively decide which obligation they will follow and which ones they will ignore, as mentioned above.

Wearing such attires by Muslim women is an assertion of their religious identity, which they carry forward from their ancestral homeland to the host society. Such assertion arises partly as a result of invasive *Wahhabism* which is propagated by Saudi Arabia with financial support and religious sponsorship. In the Western liberal and secular societies, such religious imposition is deemed offensive by many and there are arguments for it to be curtailed.

A political religious culture of Islam does not always gel harmoniously with the liberal democratic systems of the West. Rights to perform religious rites are enshrined in the law of the land, but that does not mean that all rights arising from Sharia laws, in contravention of the democratic laws of the land, should be adhered to. If religious laws encourage abrogation of the laws of the land, and no sensible compromise is possible, then those religious laws may need to be rejected by the State.

Some women wearing a niqab or burqa are now passing on such practices to their daughters – even to school-age girls. It is a common sight nowadays that Muslim girls of the age of ten or eleven wear these attires. By encouraging and enforcing such dresses on school-going daughters, they segregate these girls from their wider participation at the schools. It is a sort of voluntary acceptance of apartheid logic. If cohesion is to be improved, some religious practices based on scriptures may need to be rejected in favour of more inclusive and cohesive liberal culture.

Wearing the niqab and burqa is an abrogation of the spirit of multiculturalism. In Britain multiculturalism is encouraged as it is viewed as an all-embracing social practice. But multiculturalism does not mean, or at least should not mean, a multitude of segregated cultures and the unintentional denigration of the host culture. The continuance and perpetuation of cultural practices with strict religious underpinning, where they conflict strongly with the host custom, will continue to exacerbate social discontent and segregation.

In view of all these points, the British government should consider following the French precedent - which enforced the ban in 2010. It should be noted, however, that the religion did not prescribe wearing a burqa or niqab as obligatory. Western liberal democracy allowing individual freedom of speech, freedom of action and so forth is fine, but there must be limits to such freedom, particularly when there is a tendency for some to take undue advantage of it. If attempts are made to introduce elements of Sharia law surreptitiously under the guise of religious freedom, then such attempts should be opposed. Secularism is an unfinished project in Britain, and now, with the rise in faith schools and religious tensions and expressions, we sadly seem to be travelling in the opposite direction.

The European Court of Human Rights at Strasbourg upheld the French government's ban on wearing the burqa or niqab in its ruling on 1 July 2014. The European Court ruling stated that the ban does not breach Muslim women's human rights and consequently there is no reason why the ban should not be upheld. This is a landmark ruling, and it could prompt other European and Western countries to consider banning such attires without the risk of legal challenges.

Indeed, in March 2021, the Swiss government passed a law, after the referendum, to ban wearing a niqab or burqa or hijab by women in public. In the light of a recent developments in the Western countries, it may be time for Britain to consider banning the full-body veil, namely, the burqa and/or the niqab.

The use and abuse of science in religions

Figure 3.16   Science and Religion

Science as a whole, and religion of any description, are not always good bedfellows at the best of times. Science always retains a fair distance from religion, but religion has been found to resort to a 'pick and choose' policy towards science. That is not bad in itself; only if good, productive parts of science are assimilated in religion leaving the bad, destructive parts outside. On the other hand, if an opposite approach is taken in religion, the world will face a catastrophic situation.

When Pope Francis, head of the Catholic Church, said recently that God is not a magician with a magic wand; he was, in fact, blurting out an undeniable fact which any lesser individual than him would simply shrug away. He said, *"When we read about Creation in Genesis, we run the risk of imagining*

God was a magician with a magic wand able to do everything. But that is not so. God created human beings and let them develop according to the internal laws that he gave to each one so they would reach their fulfilment." He continued, saying, "*The big bang which today we hold to be the origin of the world, does not contradict the intervention of the divine creator but, rather, requires it. Evolution in nature is not inconsistent with the notion of creation, because evolution requires the creation of beings that evolve.*"

Pope Francis's acceptance of the big bang theory and the concept of evolution were streets ahead of the Christian churches' position even today. However, as the head of the Roman Catholic Church, he might have persuaded the Church to accept his enlightened views. Even Christianity, the most advanced and forward-looking religious system from the 15th century onwards, has been at odds with science. The Christians believed even in the 17th century that Earth was at the centre of the God's creation and all heavenly bodies revolve round the Earth. When Galileo Galilei lent his support to the previously undisclosed Copernicus' heliocentric system stating that the Sun is at the centre and Earth revolves round it, he was told that he was defying the scriptures and consequently he was found guilty of heresy. He suffered the ignominy of being a heretic and was placed under house arrest for the rest of his life.

Nonetheless, Christian churches are much more accommodating in accepting scientific ideas and developments than Judaism or Islam. That does not mean that Christian churches everywhere accept scientific developments readily. There are a large number of churches of various denominations in America where evolution is rejected even today in favour of God's creation. Intelligent Design is the buzzword for these churches. However, these rejections are not endorsed by state laws nor is there any imposition of religious beliefs by the State.

This attitude is in sharp contrast to Islamic states where the State imposes religious beliefs on the citizens. If the religious belief contradicts scientific principle, religious belief prevails. As mentioned previously, evolution does not exist in fundamentalist Muslim countries and if someone is seen propagating such ideas, that person is liable to be charged with heresy. Modern systems of government, democracy, human rights etc., are all superfluous when faced with Sharia Laws. But Sharia Laws make no pretence of compromising or adopting scientific laws and ideas; they derive legitimacy straight from the Almighty God. That way Sharia Laws claim supremacy over all man-made laws and ideas.

But the peak of the pack must now go to the inherently docile and non-martial religious belief called Hinduism. The newly elected Prime Minister of secular India, Mr Narendra Modi (NM) – the leader of the Bharatiya Janata Party (BJP) – found divine inspiration in discovering great scientific achievements in Hinduism. Who would have thought that despite the great burden of the secular state and its associated political Machiavellianism, NM would have enough time to rummage through old, dusty religious books to discover hitherto ignored or overlooked egregious scientific achievement in Hinduism?

At the inaugural ceremony of the Sir H.N. Reliance Foundation Hospital and Research Centre in Mumbai, Modi recently made public his ground-breaking discovery that since Mahabharata said Karna was not born from his mother's womb, there must have been genetic science present in India at that pre-historic time. A good logic indeed! To claim further credits to India's scientific prowess in those prehistoric days, Modi continued: since Lord Ganesh had an elephant's head on human body, it must have been that plastic surgery was prevalent in those days! With two such undeniable claims from this great leader of India, he paused to claim the laurel for India!

Narendra Modi's egregious claims are not new. He is renowned to be instrumental in introducing in the school curriculum right across Gujarat that stem cell research was known in the days of Kunti and Kausavas; television was invented during the time of Mahabharata and the motor car existed in the Vedic period! With such a litany of successes, who would have the mindset to challenge him or the country he leads?

Before Modi took charge of India, no one was aware that he was an accomplished joker, as is evident from his claims. But whatever it is, he picked up an outstandingly bad occasion to amuse and inspire his countrymen. After all, Sir H.N. Reliance Foundation Hospital and Research Centre, which he was inaugurating, was not the right place to tell jokes – the centre was supposed to be the cutting-edge research centre in medical sciences in India. Now talking about jokes, a similar joke can be presented here:

An Egyptian, a Chinese and an Indian were arguing about the antiquity of their civilisation. First the Egyptian said proudly, "Recently we dug 250 feet below ground in our barren deserts and we found golden statues. Our civilisation was that old and advanced enough to produce golden statues."

"That is nothing," said the Chinese dismissively, "We dug 500 feet below ground and we found man-size soldiers guarding our palaces at that time. We had civilised society even at that time."

The Indian had been listening patiently so far. Then he said in a quiet, contemplative manner, "Look, we dug well over 1000 feet below ground and we found absolutely nothing."

"What does that mean?" screamed the other two in unison.

"It means," the Indian continued in an assertive tone, "it means that even at that time we had wireless communication!"

Now Narendra Modi may have a streak of that Indian character, but he has brought a whole new ball game to the fore. He may be implicitly claiming his position at the topmost table of scientifically advanced countries when India had genetic science, plastic surgery, television etc., not now, but nearly four millennia ago!

But, more crucially, he seems to have a game plan. Whereas all the religions – Islam or Christianity or Judaism and so forth –

endeavour to bring scriptures and divine messages into the modern age by fitting scientific developments into religions, Narendra Modi is asserting that his religion was in harmony with present day scientific developments back at the time of Mahabharata's creation, because all of these scientific things were present at that time. His religion was going hand in hand with science right from the time of creation of Earth!

Narendra Modi has drawn inspiration from his mendacious claims of spectacular achievements in science in India in those prehistoric days and is carrying on with his religious beliefs in modern times to run the country. For Narendra Modi bright days may lie ahead; but for India, democracy and secularism are in the sick bed.

Albert Einstein's views on religion

Many people, particularly those promoting and spreading religious beliefs (in all major religions), have over the years laid claims that Albert Einstein was a man of religious conviction. They often put forward Einstein's famous quote, *"God does not play dice"*, to lay claims that belief in God's determinism and absolutism in creation was inbuilt in Einstein's thought process. Nothing, it may be emphasised, nothing, could be furthest from the truth and Einstein's inner thoughts.

Albert Einstein was not a man of religious conviction by any standards. His views, if considered dispassionately, would verge on the side of atheism; although he did not like to be branded as an 'atheist'. His views on religions were very well articulated in his one-and-a-half-page letter, written in the German language in 1954 (just a year before his death) to the German philosopher, Eric Gutkind, which contained, *"The word God is for me nothing more than the expression and product of human weaknesses, the Bible a collection of honourable but still primitive legends, which are nevertheless pretty childish."* He also said, *"No interpretation, no matter how subtle, can change this."* That letter was sold in an auction at Christie's in New York in 2018 for the staggering sum of $2.9 million (£2.3 million).

That "God does not play dice" was not stated by Einstein out of devotion to God, but as a riposte to the flagbearers of 'Copenhagen interpretation' headed by Niels Bohr and supported by Heisenberg, Max Planck and others on quantum mechanics. Although Albert Einstein and Max Planck were the pioneers of the quantum concept in the first decade of the 20th century, subsequent developments of quantum mechanics by Niels Bohr/Schrodinger/Heisenberg/Pauli/Dirac and many more, leading to the probabilistic nature of elementary particles were very much disliked and disputed by Einstein. An object is either there or not, it cannot be half there and half not; Einstein

269

contended. In that context, he rejected the probabilistic nature of particles by that quote of 'playing dice'. He also said, " *The moon is there in the night sky whether we observe it or not. Just because we cannot observe the moon because of cloud in the sky does not mean the moon is not there!"*

However, quantum physics was relentlessly moving ahead with probabilistic interpretation of objects and successfully explained many hitherto inexplicable physical phenomena. Einstein struggled at the latter part of his life with the nature of reality. When Tagore and Einstein met in Berlin in 1926 (and at least three more times until their 1930 meeting in New York), they had a very fascinating philosophical discussion/debate, not so much on the existence of God but on the nature of reality. Tagore held the Eastern philosophical view of convergence of man (meaning life) and nature, while Einstein held the view of 'absolutism' (although he was the father of 'Relativity' and 'Quantum Mechanics').

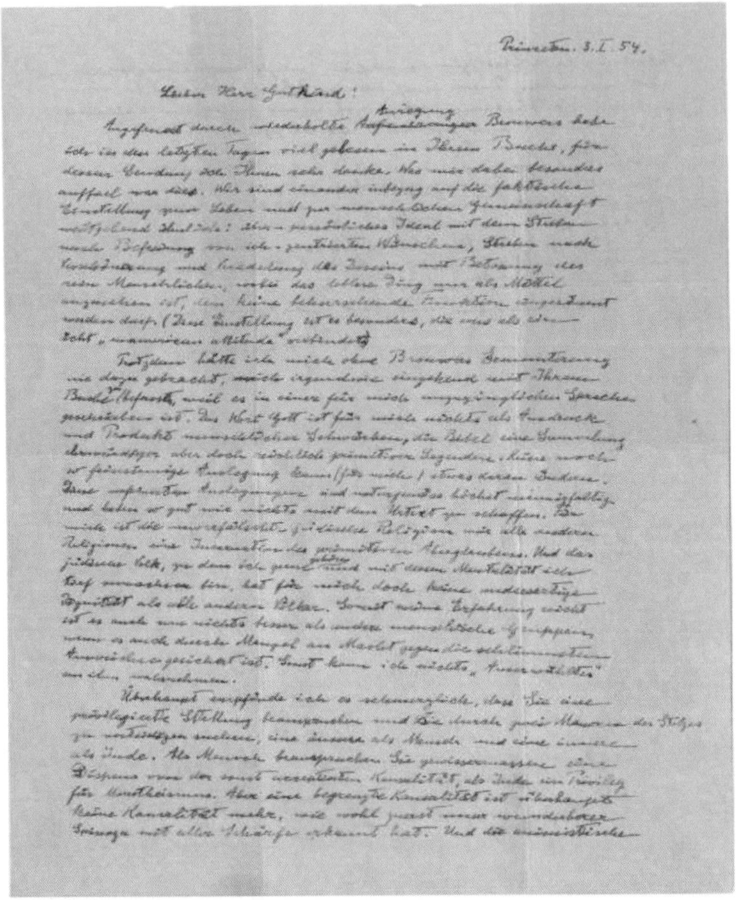

Princeton. 3. I. 54.

Lieber Herr Gutkind!

Figure 3.17 Einstein's hand-written letter in Germany giving his views on Judaism

In the letter, Einstein, an Ashkenazi Jew, also articulated his disenchantment with Judaism. *"For me the Jewish religion like all others is an incarnation of the most childish superstitions. And the Jewish people to whom I gladly belong and with whose mentality I have a deep affinity have no different quality for me than all other people,"* he wrote.

Figure 3.18   *Einstein as a boy and as a man about to publish the*
special theory of relativity

However, as a child he was religious, as is the case with most of the children of religious families anywhere in the world. But he had a fiercely independent mind and a deeply inquisitive character. He disliked authoritarian attitudes – whether in teaching or training. He was very unhappy at the Luitpold Gymnasium (a strict discipline-focussed school) in Munich, where his parents enrolled him for proper education. He described later that he deeply disliked the 'rote learning' method at the school, with no opportunity for creative thinking. He, however, remained at that school to keep his parents happy. Years later, he advised people, "*Learn from yesterday, live for today, hope for tomorrow. The important thing is not to stop questioning.*"

Einstein did not or could not completely discard the notion of the supremacy of the supernatural power, which became inbuilt in his childhood, although he rejected consciously the idea that this religion or that religion derives from the orders or messages from God. By the age of 13, he started doubting the religious teachings and *"abandoned his uncritical religious fervour, feeling he had been deceived into believing lies."*

He believed in, or had strong inclination towards, "Spinoza's God" (Baruch Spinoza, a 17th century Dutch thinker), *"who reveals himself in the lawful harmony of the world, not in a God who concerns himself with the fate and the doings of mankind."* Einstein had the same or similar mindset. This streak of thinking had a strong resonance with the Eastern philosophy that man and nature merge into one or have a strong interconnection.

The physical world follows a set of laws and principles with specific physical constants relevant to the natural world. Any variation of these laws and constants would negate the existence of this universe and could possibly generate another universe. That may be the underlying thinking in the idea of multiverse. So, to claim that a grand designer created this universe with specific set rules and laws for our habitation in mind was a mendacious presumption to Einstein.

Einstein was, to a large extent, ambivalent about God, the so-called grand designer. He could neither prove nor disprove the existence of this 'Uncaused Cause', the 'Unmoved Mover' and hence it was sensible to maintain some ambivalence; but all his instincts were against such a presumption. He said facetiously, *"I want to know how God created this world. I am not interested in this or that phenomenon, in the spectrum of this or that element. I want to know His thoughts; the rest are details."*

Glossary of Terms

Abbasid Caliphate The Abbasid Caliphate was the third caliphate to succeed prophet Mohammad. It was founded by a dynasty descended from prophet Mohammad's uncle, Abbas Abdul-Muttalib from whom the dynasty takes the name. They ruled from their capital in Baghdad after having overthrown the Umayyad Caliphate (661 CE to 750 CE) from 750 CE to 1258 CE. This caliphate was blatantly anti-rationalist and held the view that rationalism is anti-Islamic.

Abdus Salam Professor Mohammad Abdus Salam (1926 – 1996) was a theoretical physicist of Pakistani heritage, who shared the 1979 Nobel Prize in Physics with Sheldon Glashow and Steven Weinberg for their contribution to the electroweak interactions. He was a Muslim of Ahmadiyya (also known as Qadiani) denomination, after the founder Mirza Ghulam Ahmad Qadian in 1889. Ahmadiyya is more aligned to the Sunni sect of Islam than to the Shia sect.

Abrahamic Religions Abrahamic religions are those which derive from the preaching of Prophet Abraham (or Ibrahim in Islam), where one supreme God is proclaimed and that is why they are also called monotheistic religions. Three major religions of the world – Judaism, Christianity and Islam come from Abrahamic preaching. The Abrahamic God was Elah, from where Allah was derived in Islam.

Age of Enlightenment The period spanning from the 17th to 19th centuries when Europe moved away from vicious religious conflicts and embraced reasons (also known as the Age of Reason). This is the period when science and technology were embraced in Europe, the Industrial Revolution took place and

European civilisation streamed ahead of the rest of the world.

Alawite A subsect of Shia Islam, which is regarded by Sunni as heretical. It is located primarily in Syria where it makes up approximately 12 per cent of the population. The present president of Syria, Bashar al-Assad is from the Alawite sect.

Allah Abraham's (Ibrahim's) God was Elah, where from Islam's Allah is derived.

Apostate A person who renounces his or her previous religious beliefs. In Islam, an apostasy is a crime punishable by death.

Arab Spring Arab Spring refers to a series of anti-government protests and uprisings, which started in the spring of 2011 in Tunisia, against corruption, oppression, low standards of living and above all, lack of democratic rights. The Tunisian uprising caused the downfall of the government and that encouraged other Arab countries such as Libya, Egypt, Yemen, Syria, Bahrain and so forth to follow suit. In some cases such as Libya, Syria and Yemen bitter civil war ensued.

Ash'arités Ash'arités are the followers of Islamic theology which was founded by Abu as-Hasan al-Ash'ari from Basra in the 10th century. He advanced the orthodox form of religion that the sacred book of Quran is eternal and uncreated and must be followed. The Ash'ari school had followers like al-Ghazali and Ibn Khaldūn who were vehemently against the Mu'tazili rationalist views.

BCE Before the Common Era. BCE replaces the previously used term Before Christ (BC).

Blasphemy Blasphemy is an impious utterance or disrespectful action against God or Allah and contempt towards other

276

religious beliefs. It was introduced by British colonial rulers in the 19th century purportedly to stop inter-religious conflicts. But now those blasphemy laws are vigorously used in the decolonised Muslim States to suppress people for political purposes.

Burqa, Niqab and Hijab   The 'burqa' is a garment for women to envelop the whole of the woman's body, from head to toe, with a mesh cloth over the eyes to see. A burqa is normally made of black cloth, though recently other colours are also used.

A 'niqab' is similar to a burqa but with a thin slit, instead of mesh cloth, for the eyes. A niqab is also predominantly black in colour. The Grand Mufti of al-Azhar mosque came out strongly in 2013 against the niqab, saying that it is an un-Islamic practice. He had made his female students of a college remove their niqab against the wishes of some of the students.

The 'hijab' is, on the other hand, a headgear that is wrapped around the head covering the head, neck and shoulders with only the face exposed.

Caliphate (Islamic)   An Islamic state where Sharia is the basis of governance. It is used mainly with reference to past Islamic empires in the Middle East.

Canaan   Canaan was a Semitic speaking region in the 2nd millennium BCE covering present-day Israel, West Bank and Gaza, Jordan, the southern part of Lebanon and Syria. The name Canaan appears throughout the Bible.

CE   Common Era. This is the same as Anno Domini (AD) but without the religious connotation.

Darwinism   Darwinism is the theory of biological evolution developed by Charles Darwin, an English naturalist, in the 19th century, that all species of organisms develop through natural selection. He stated that all life forms go through a struggle for existence and there is survival of the fittest.

Ekushey   Ekushey is the Bengali word referring to the number 21. On this day, 21st of February in 1952, police fired on a students' demonstration demanding Bengali to be given the status of state language and killed seven students. This day also epitomises the start of the Bangladeshi national movement and Bangladeshi nationalism. Ekushey had been declared as the International Mother Language Day by the United Nations Educational, Scientific and Cultural Organisation (UNESCO) in November 1999, which was then endorsed by the UN General Assembly in 2002.

Free Syrian Army (FSA)   The FSA, founded in July 2011, was a loose federation of Syrian Army defectors whose stated aim was to bring down the government of Bashar al-Asaad and then the Syrian civil war started. Although outwardly FSA stated that they wanted to establish democracy in Syria, it was a conflict between Shia and Sunni sects. The Sunni group was supported by Saudi Arabia, Qatar, UAE as well as Turkey and America, whereas the Shia group was supported by Iran and militia groups in Iraq and Lebanon.

Ghazali   Abu Hamid al-Ghazali (1058–1111) was a prominent Muslim philosopher and theologian of Sunni Islam from Persia. He was an anti-rationalist dogmatic philosopher who wrote the book *Tahafut al-Falasifa (Incoherence of the Philosophers)* where he denounced enlightened Muslim philosophers and preached that knowledge should only be sought in the Quran! In response, Ibu Rushd (1126–1198), an Andalusian Muslim philosopher, theologian and Islamic jurisprudence and linguist, wrote *The Incoherence of Incoherence* where he highlighted the fallacy and incoherence of Ghazali philosophy.

Golden Age of Islam This is the period in Islamic history between the 8th century and the middle of the 13th century when Islam attained the pinnacle of glory in science and technology, art and culture, music and medicine and so forth.

Islamic State (IS) The territory occupied by the Jihadists in Syria, Iraq and Kurdistan was declared as the Islamic State (IS).

Khorasan Khorasan was the region that included Persia, part of Afghanistan and part of Central Asia. It was an influential region during the Golden Age of Islam.

Makkah A city in the Kingdom of Saudi Arabia, where Kabaa, Masjid-e-Haram, the most sacred mosque in Islam is situated. The city is barred for non-Muslims to visit. In English, Makkah is written as Mecca.

Meme The word 'meme' was coined by Professor Richard Dawkins, an Evolutionary Biologist, to convey a similar sense to the word 'gene'. A meme is the replicator of cultural transmission as a gene is the replicator of a biological unit. *"Just as genes propagate themselves in the gene pool by leaping from body to body via sperms or eggs, so memes propagate themselves in the meme pool by leaping from brain to brain via a process which can be called imitation."*

Monotheistic religions The religions that hold the belief that there is only one God. The three major monotheistic religions are Judaism, Christianity and Islam. Other monotheistic religions are Zoroastrianism and Sikhism. Even in Hinduism, there is a belief that although there are many gods and goddesses, there is one supreme God who rules over these minor gods and goddesses.

Muslim Brotherhood This is a transnational Sunni Islamist movement founded in Egypt in 1928 by Hasan al-Banna that seeks to implement Sharia-based law in all Muslim countries. Many Muslim countries adopt the principle of Muslim Brotherhood but take different names to implement the principle. They propagate their Islamist philosophy quietly, through economic activity and charity.

Mu'tazilites Mu'tazilites are the followers of a rationalist school of Islamic theology which flourished during the Abbasid caliphate in Baghdad during the 'Golden Age' of Islam. The Mu'tazili school of Kalam (knowledge) considered the injunctions of God to be accessible to rational thought and inquiry and that reason, not 'sacred precedent' is the effective means to determine what is just and religiously obligatory.

Renaissance The Renaissance was the period – 15th and 16th century – when Europe moved away from the crises of the Middle Ages to the modern ages when the Age of Reason was ushered in and conditions were created for the Age of Enlightenment.

Sharia Laws A legal framework in Islam to regulate public and private aspects of life on specific Islamic teaching. Sharia is a strict system which views non-Muslims as second-class citizens, sanctions inequality between men and women and to a large extent violates Human Rights.

Shia The second largest sect in Islam (after Sunni).

Sunni Sunni is the main sect of Islam, which constitutes between 85 to 90 per cent of Islam. This sect believes that Abu Bakr, the father of Mohammad's wife Aisha, was Mohammad's rightful successor.

Survival machine   The survival machine for the selfish genes is the human body itself, as described by Prof. Richard Dawkins in his book, *The Selfish Gene*. Genes try to keep the body alive as without it the genes will die.

Two Nation Theory (TNT)   The Two Nation Theory (TNT) asserted that Hindus and Muslims in India do not belong to one nation but two separate nations with their separate customs, traditions, education, economic conditions and religions. This theory was advanced by Allama Iqbal in 1930 and then it was adopted by the All India Muslim League conference in Lahore in 1940 and Mohammad Ali Jinnah adopted it as the founding principle of the Pakistan Movement.

Umayyad Caliphate   The Umayyad Caliphate from 661 CE to 750 CE, having Damascus as the capital, was responsible for the start of the Islamic Golden Age. After the Umayyad Caliphate, the Abbasid Caliphate from 751 CE to 1258 CE, having Baghdad as the capital, ruled the last part of the Golden Age.

Wahhabism/Salafism   Wahhabism as a doctrine is based on the preaching of Mohammad ibn Abd al-Wahhab of Saudi Arabia in the 18th century. Salafism is wider than Wahhabism and existed for hundreds of years. This theology insists on strict Quranic interpretation and preaches that those who do not practice their form of Islam are heathens. This fundamentalist ideology has actually helped to create IS or ISIS and is the root of all Islamic terrorism.

Recommendations for KEEPING UP WITH TIME

The author has established himself as an essayist of wide erudition, astute judgments, and provocative insights. Anchored in an enlightened worldview with a steadfast commitment to reason and human progress, his brief pieces are accessible, enjoyable, and educational. This collection of essays is particularly welcome at a time when the intellectual environment in the world is being muddied by false and frothy claims that confuse and mislead people.

Professor Ahrar Ahmad
Director General, Gyantapas Abdur Razzaq Foundation
Professor Emeritus, Black Hills State University,
South Dakota, USA

It is a great pleasure to read the book comprising a mind-boggling array of thought-provoking articles. The topics range from science and technology to religion and philosophical, social and political issues and many more. The readers will definitely benefit from the author's in-depth knowledge and unbiased analyses.

Professor Quamrul Haider,
Department of Physics and Engineering Physics,
Fordham University, New York, USA

282